Chapter Test

Reviewing Vocabulary

Match each vocabulary word to a picture.

_____d_____ **1.** bacteria

a.

_____c_____ **2.** protist

b.

_____b_____ **3.** invertebrate

c.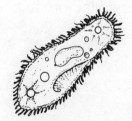

_____a_____ **4.** fungi

d.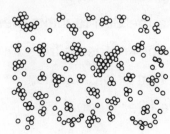

Complete each sentence with the correct vocabulary word.

5. Mosses are examples of ____nonvascular____ plants.

6. A(n) ____angiosperm____ is a vascular plant that produces flowers.

7. All animals that have a backbone are called ____vertebrates____.

Checking Main Ideas

Circle the letter of the best answer.

8. How are plants different from fungi?

   A Plant cells have cell walls.   **C** Plants are multicellular.

   B Plants can make their own food.   **D** Plant cells have a nucleus.

9. Which animals are vertebrates?

   A cnidarians   **C** amphibians

   B arthropods   **D** echinoderms

10. What reproductive structures do gymnosperms produce?

   A flowers   **C** cones

   B spores   **D** fruit

11. Which are single-celled organisms whose cells do not contain nuclei?

   A bacteria   **C** invertebrates

   B protists   **D** algae

12. How do fungi obtain food?

   A They use the Sun to make their own food.

   B They absorb nutrients from the environment.

   C They eat other organisms.

   D They are filter feeders.

Using Inquiry Skills

Answer the questions using complete sentences.

13. Infer A small plant only grows to about 2 inches in height. The plant cannot grow unless it is living very close to a water source. Is this plant a vascular plant or a nonvascular plant? Why?

It is a nonvascular plant because nonvascular plants do not have

specialized tube-like tissues to carry water like vascular plants do.

This is why they are always small and must live near water.

14. Use Models What type(s) of symmetry does this organism have? How do you know?

The organism has radial symmetry, because its body

parts are arranged equally around a middle point.

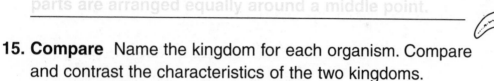

15. Compare Name the kingdom for each organism. Compare and contrast the characteristics of the two kingdoms.

The *E. coli* bacterium is in the Kingdom Eubacteria. Diatoms are in

Kingdom Protista. Bacteria are single-celled organisms that do not have

nuclei. Most protists are single-celled organisms that possess nuclei.

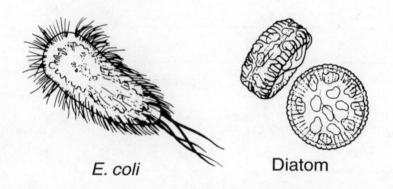

E. coli   Diatom

16. Ask Questions A scientist is examining a new species of plant. She needs to determine which group the plant belongs to. Make a simple dichotomous key she can use to further classify the plant.

Does it have vascular tissue?

    no ⟶ hornwort, moss, or liverwort

    yes ⟶ go to question 2

Does it produce seeds?

    no ⟶ horsetail or fern

    yes ⟶ go to question 3

Does it produce flowers or fruits?

    no ⟶ gymnosperm

    yes ⟶ angiosperm

Thinking Critically

Answer the questions using complete sentences.

17. **Analyze** Ameobas and algae are both protists. Why are they classified into different groups within this kingdom?

Amoebas are animal-like protists. They cannot make their own food. They can move through their environment. Algae are plant-like protists. They can make their own food through photosynthesis.

18. **Evaluate** Which characteristics of reptiles allow them to live on land?

They have a dry skin with a waterproof coating that helps them conserve water. They are able to reproduce on land because their eggs have a tough outer coating that keeps them from drying out.

19. **Apply** Compare and contrast sponges and cnidarians.

Both are invertebrate animals. Both live in water. Sponges have no tissues, organs, or symmetry. Cnidarians are more complex. Cnidarians have radial symmetry.

20. **Synthesize** Explain how a dichotomous key helps scientists classify organisms.

The key gives two characteristics to choose between. Each choice leads to another pair of characteristics and narrows down the possibility of what an organism can be.

Name _____ Date _____

Chapter Test

Reviewing Vocabulary
Circle the letter of the best answer.

1. Which cells surround and consume harmful organisms that invade the body?

   A antibodies   **C** epithelial cells

   B phagocytes   **D** hormones

2. Which system carries oxygen in the body?

   A endocrine system   **C** circulatory system

   B skeletal system   **D** nervous system

Complete each sentence with the correct vocabulary word.

3. The process that spreads substances through a gas or liquid is _____diffusion_____.

4. Leaves, roots, and flowers are all examples of a plant's _____organs_____.

5. A _____contagious_____ disease is one that can be spread easily from one person to another.

6. The control center of the cell is the _____nucleus_____.

7. A sugar that plants produce through photosynthesis is _____glucose_____.

Checking Main Ideas
For each statement, circle the word _True_ or the word _False_. Rewrite each false statement to make it true.

8. A group of organs that work together to perform a complex task is a tissue.

   True   (False)

   A group of organs that work together is an organ system.

9. Inflammation is one of the body's defenses against disease.

(True)   False

_____

10. The endocrine system controls all other organ systems in the body.

True   (False)

The brain (or nervous system) controls all other organ systems.

11. The diagram shows diffusion across the cell membrane of a cell.

True   (False)

The diagram shows active transport.

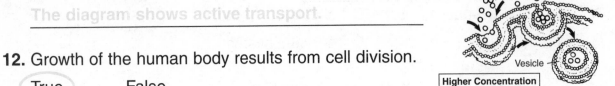

Molecules | Lower Concentration

Vesicle

Higher Concentration

12. Growth of the human body results from cell division.

(True)   False

_____

Using Inquiry Skills

Answer the questions using complete sentences.

Vaccine	Number of People Who Received Vaccine	Number of People Who Got Sick
A	200	50
B	50	7
C	90	10

13. Analyze Data Several vaccines, Vaccine A, Vaccine B, and
Vaccine C, were tested. All of the people who participated were the
same age and had the same health history. The table shows how
many people in each group got sick from the disease after being
given a vaccination. Which vaccine was the most effective against
the disease? How do you know?

Vaccine C was most effective because this group had the

smallest percentage of people who got sick.

14. Use Variables What is the dependent variable in this experiment?

The number of people who got sick after getting the vaccine.

15. Predict Particles are moving by diffusion across the cell membrane. In which direction will the particles move?

They will move from areas of high concentration to areas of low concentration, so they will move out of the cell.

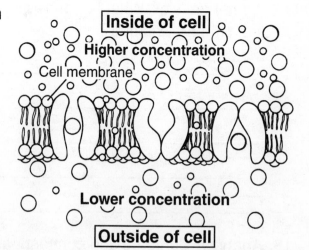

Thinking Critically

Answer the questions using complete sentences.

16. Evaluate Explain how photosynthesis and respiration are related.

Photosynthesis uses energy, carbon dioxide, and water to produce oxygen and glucose. Respiration is the reverse reaction in which oxygen and glucose are broken down into water, carbon dioxide, and energy.

17. Synthesize Explain how the circulatory system and the respiratory system work together to supply the body with oxygen and remove carbon dioxide.

Oxygen enters the body through the respiratory system. Oxygen in the lungs diffuses into the blood. Blood, transported in vessels, carries oxygen to all parts of the body. Blood carrying carbon dioxide travels to the lungs. Carbon dioxide diffuses out of the blood and into the lungs. Carbon dioxide is exhaled.

18. **Draw Conclusions** Johann had chicken pox, which is caused by a virus, when he was in second grade. Several years later, many of his classmates became ill with the chicken pox. Although Johann was exposed to the virus a second time, he did not get sick. What happened in Johann's immune system the first time he was sick?

Antibodies were produced that recognize the virus that

causes chicken pox. Those antibodies fought the virus the

second time.

_____

19. **Analyze** Compare and contrast passive transport and active transport.

Both involve substances moving across a cell membrane.

In passive transport, no energy is used and substances

move from areas of high to low concentration. In active

transport, energy is used and substances move from areas

of low to high concentration.

20. **Apply** A person breathes in air that contains harmful bacteria. Which part of the first line of defense should help prevent the person from being infected?

Mucus in the nose is part of the first line of defense.

_____

Chapter Test

Reviewing Vocabulary

For each statement, circle the word _True_ or the word _False_.
Rewrite each false statement to make it true.

1. Bacterial fission is an example of sexual reproduction.

   True   (False)

   Bacterial fission is an example of asexual reproduction.
   _____

2. A permanent change in a gene or a chromosome is called a mutation.

   (True)   False

   _____

Complete each sentence with the correct vocabulary word.

3. The stage in the cell cycle in which the nucleus divides is _____ mitosis _____ .

4. A _____ hybrid _____ is the offspring of two parents from different purebred strains.

5. The cell structures on which proteins are made are _____ ribosomes _____ .

6. During _____ sexual reproduction _____ , two parents produce offspring that inherit traits from each parent.

Checking Main Ideas

Complete each sentence with the correct term.

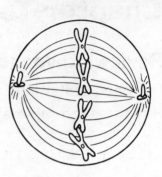

7. The phase of mitosis shown in the diagram is
   _____metaphase_____ .

8. The phase of mitosis that follows the one shown in the
   diagram is_____anaphase_____ .

Circle the letter of the best answer.

9. What is the name of the process of copying DNA to pass it on to
   offspring?

   A reproduction   **C** replication

   B transcription   **D** translation

10. Which are produced during sexual reproduction?

    A gametes   **C** spores

    B buds   **D** rhizomes

11. During which phase of mitosis do spindle fibers form?

    A prophase   **C** anaphase

    B metaphase   **D** telophase

Using Inquiry Skills

Answer the questions using complete sentences.

12. **Predict** In pea plants, the allele for tall plants (*T*) is dominant
    over the allele for short plants (*t*). Complete the Punnett square
    below for two pea plants. Predict the percentage of the offspring
    that will be tall and the percentage of offspring that will be short.

	T	*T*
T	TT	TT
t	Tt	Tt

    Tall = 100%, Short = 0%

Name _____ Date _____

13. Apply Explain whether the following statement is true or false: All mutations to DNA are harmful.

The statement is false. Some mutations can be beneficial

to organisms; for example, one type of mutation causes

strawberry plants to make very large fruits.

14. Hypothesize While at the park, you observe that one species of rose can produce flowers that are white, yellow, red, and pink. Make a hypothesis about how this species can produce different colored flowers.

The plant has alleles for each color of flower.

_____

_____

15. Experiment Design an experiment in which you could test the hypothesis you made for question 14. How could you determine which alleles are dominant or recessive?

The experiment should include the idea of starting with

purebred plants, then cross-breeding to determine which

alleles are dominant and which are recessive.

Thinking Critically

Answer the questions using complete sentences.

16. Evaluate What effect would the improper functioning of mRNA have on the process of protein production?

The process of protein production cannot occur unless

mRNA transfers the genetic information in DNA from the

nucleus of the original cell.

_____

17. Analyze Compare and contrast mitosis and meiosis.

Mitosis is part of the cell cycle in which cells divide. During mitosis,

the nucleus and cytoplasm divide once and two new cells are

produced. These cells have the same DNA as the parent cells. Meiosis

results in the formation of gametes. The parent cell divides twice and

the gametes have copies of half of the parent's chromosomes. When

gametes unite, the new set has two complete sets of chromosomes.

18. Draw Conclusions In humans, two dominant alleles for blood types can be written as I^A and I^B. These alleles are codominant. A person with alleles $I^A I^A$ has blood type A. A person with alleles $I^B I^B$ has blood type B. What would be the blood type of a person with alleles $I^A I^B$?

Blood type AB

19. Synthesize Make a chart on the back of this paper that shows the steps of the cell cycle, including the phases of mitosis.

Charts will vary but should include all the steps of the cell

cycle: Interphase; Mitosis (prophase, metaphase, anaphase,

telophase); Cytokinesis.

20. Apply How do DNA and RNA differ?

RNA has the base uracil instead of thymine. RNA is a

single strand, not double.

Chapter Test

Reviewing Vocabulary

Complete each sentence with the correct vocabulary word.

1. The practice of choosing organisms with desirable traits to reproduce is known as ___selective breeding___ .

2. ___Extinction___ is the death of all members of a species.

3. ___Homologous___ structures are similar body structures on different species.

4. A ___fossil___ is the preserved remains or trace of an organism that lived long ago.

Match each definition to the correct vocabulary word.

5. a large number of species die at about the same time

6. consists of the Precambrian, Paleozoic, Mezozoic, and Cenozoic Eras

7. organisms better adapted to their environment survive and reproduce

natural selection

mass extinction

geologic time scale

Checking Main Ideas

Answer the questions using complete sentences.

8. What kind of fossil is this? How does it form?

It is an imprint fossil. An imprint fossil is an

impression in soft mud or sediment that

hardens into rock.

9. What do fossils reveal?

Fossils provide a record of Earth's living things, and they

are evidence for changes among them.

10. What do paleontologists do?

They dig up and study fossils. They compare fossil

organisms with living organisms today. They make models

of ancient animals by studying the remains of the animals.

11. Give two examples of how bacteria are still evolving today.

Bacteria are evolving to resist antibacterial soaps. They

are also becoming resistant to many antibiotics, including

penicillin.

For each statement, circle the word *True* or the word *False*. Rewrite each false statement to make it true.

12. Charles Darwin developed the theory of selective breeding.

True   (False)

Charles Darwin developed the theory of natural selection.

13. Some fossils are formed from hardened tree sap called amber.

(True)   False

_____

14. This fossil provided evidence that the first bird species developed from amphibians.

True   (False)

Archaeopteryx is evidence that the first

bird species developed from reptiles.

_____

Name _____ Date _____

Using Inquiry Skills

Answer the questions using complete sentences.

15. Infer How did this fossil likely form?

This is an insect trapped in amber, which is hardened tree

sap. The insect most likely got stuck in the tree sap. The sap later hardened.

16. Classify Complete the table using the names of the organisms in the box.

| early fish | primates | dinosaurs | bacteria | amphibians |
| early reptiles | flowering plants | humans | fungi | reptiles |

Precambrian Era	Paleozoic Era	Mesozoic Era	Cenozoic Era
bacteria	early fish	dinosaurs	primates
fungi	early reptiles	flowering plants	humans
	amphibians	reptiles	

Thinking Critically

Answer the questions using complete sentences.

17. Draw Conclusions On a voyage to several remote islands, you observe a different species of turtle on each island. The turtles are nearly identical, except the shapes of their shells. What can you conclude about the evolution of the shell in these turtle species?

The shell shape of each turtle species evolved over time,

because the environment and/or food supplies on each

island were different.

18. Apply Bacteria are evolving to resist certain antibiotic medicines. Describe in terms of natural selection how this could be happening.

Some individuals in the bacteria population have a

resistance to antibiotics. These individuals are better

adapted to the environment. They reproduce and pass their

genes to the next generation. Over time, more individuals

have the resistance.

19. Analyze Scientists have discovered 3-million-year-old footprints of human ancestors in Africa. Describe three kinds of information these fossils might reveal about our ancestors.

Answers may vary. The fossils could reveal how big our

ancestors were. The fossils could reveal how fast our

ancestors walked. The fossils could reveal information

about the environment at the time. The fossils could reveal

if our ancestors walked like modern people.

Chapter Test

Reviewing Vocabulary

Complete each sentence with the correct vocabulary word.

1. In the process of ____respiration____, oxygen and glucose are combined to make carbon dioxide and water.

2. This diagram shows two kinds of ____precipitation____.

3. ____Decomposers____ are organisms that break apart dead organic matter into simpler parts.

4. The process by which water evaporates through a plant's leaves is ____transpiration____.

5. Water consumes energy during ____evaporation____ and changes from the liquid state to the gas state.

6. During ____photosynthesis____, plants use energy from the Sun to change carbon dioxide and water into glucose and oxygen.

Circle the letter of the best answer.

7. What is the process of changing nitrogen gas into useful nitrogen compounds?

   A decomposition

   B sedimentation

   C nitrogen fixation

   D nitrogen carbonation

8. Each step in the movement of energy through an ecosystem is known as a(n)

A trophic level

B autotroph

C consumer

D producer

Checking Main Ideas

**For each statement, circle the word *True* or the word *False*.
Rewrite each false statement to make it true.**

9. Living things are made up mostly of carbon dioxide.

True   False

Living things are made up mostly of water.

10. Primary consumers feed directly on producers.

True   False

_____

11. Most nitrogen fixation uses the energy released by lightning.

True   False

Most nitrogen fixation results from the actions of special bacteria.

Circle the letter of the best answer.

12. Which process is NOT part of the water cycle?

A precipitation

B condensation

C transpiration

D conservation

13. Which adds to the amount of carbon dioxide in the atmosphere?

   A planting new forests

   B burning fossil fuels

   C global warming

   D acid rain

14. Which is a producer in an ecosystem?

   A a lion   B a rabbit

   C a tree   D the Sun

Using Inquiry Skills

Answer the questions using complete sentences.

15. Predict Suppose that the number of secondary consumers in an ecosystem increased. How might this change affect other organisms in this ecosystem?

If the number of secondary consumers increased, they would eat all of the primary consumers. The secondary consumers would then have no food, which could cause their populations to get smaller.

16. Infer A forest is being cleared to build new houses. What might happen to the levels of carbon dioxide in the air?

With fewer trees, less carbon dioxide would be removed from the atmosphere. Over time, the level of carbon dioxide in the air might start to build up.

17. Analyze Describe the role of trees and other plants in the water cycle.

During transpiration, water evaporates from the leaves of plants and enters the atmosphere as water vapor. Water vapor will condense to form clouds. Eventually, the water will fall back to Earth's surface as precipitation.

Thinking Critically

Answer the questions using complete sentences.

18. **Draw Conclusions** These two plants were planted at the same time. They have received the same amount of water and the same amount of sunlight. What might be a reason why Plant B is so much taller than Plant A? How might you improve Plant A's growth?

Plant A may not be getting as much nitrogen as Plant B.

Plant A's growth might be improved by adding nitrogen-rich

fertilizer to the soil.

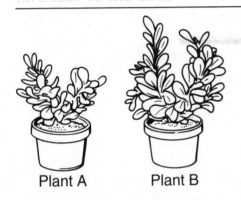

Plant A   Plant B

19. **Apply** What might happen if all of the algae in the world's oceans suddenly stopped carrying out photosynthesis?

Most of Earth's oxygen comes from photosynthetic algae in the

oceans. If these algae were unable to carry out photosynthesis,

the atmosphere would have much less oxygen.

20. **Analyze** Describe the meaning of this statement: *Energy moves in one direction through the trophic levels of a food chain, from producers to consumers.*

Plants get energy from the Sun and use this energy to make food.

Animals eat plants and other animals to get energy. Because plants

are producers and animals are consumers, energy in a food chain

moves in just one direction, from the Sun to plants to animals.

Chapter Test

Reviewing Vocabulary

Complete each sentence with the correct vocabulary word.

1. A type of symbiosis in which one species benefits while the other species is neither helped nor harmed is called _____commensalism_____ .

2. A large group of similar ecosystems that share a similar climate is called a(n) _____biome_____ .

3. The type of consumer that eats only the food shown in the picture is a(n) _____herbivore_____ .

4. Two animals are in a symbiotic relationship in which both of them benefit. This relationship is called _____mutualism_____ .

Circle the letter of the best answer.

5. A(n)_____ consists of all of the living and nonliving things in an area.

 A biome

 B ecosystem

 C niche

 D abiotic factor

6. Which phrase best describes symbiosis?

 A a close living relationship between two different species

 B a close living relationship between two members of the same species

 C a relationship where one species relies upon another species as food

 D a relationship where one species serves as food for another species

7. Describe the relationship between a predator and its prey.

In a predator–prey relationship, the predator hunts and eats

its prey.

8. What are three abiotic factors in an ecosystem?

temperature, precipitation, wind, soil, water, rocks, sunlight

Checking Main Ideas

**For each statement, circle the word *True* or the word *False*.
Rewrite each false statement to make it true.**

9. The tundra is one of Earth's warmer biomes.

True   (False)

The tundra is one of Earth's colder biomes.

10. Every species occupies more than one niche in its ecosystem.

True   (False)

Every species occupies one niche in its ecosystem.

11. Humans can be involved in symbiotic relationships with other species.

(True)   False

_____

Circle the letter of the best answer.

12. Which two organisms can have a relationship of parasitism?

A hippopotamus and oxpecker bird

B sea anemone and clownfish

C alga and fungus

D human and tapeworm

13. Which biome is characterized by grasses, few trees, frequent fires, and relatively little rain?

   A grassland   **B** taiga

   C tundra   **D** temperate forest

14. Which biological process describes how an insecticide such as DDT becomes concentrated in animals such as hawks?

   A transfer of nutrients   **B** predation

   C biomagnification   **D** symbiosis

Using Inquiry Skills

Answer the questions using complete sentences.

15. Infer A particular biome has an average rainfall of 2.5 centimeters per year and an average temperature of 20°C. What kind of biome is it?

This is a desert because it receives very little rainfall and its average temperature is relatively high.

16. Compare An animal, such as a raccoon, that eats many types of food is called a generalist. An animal, such as a giraffe, that eats just one type of food is called a specialist. Which type of animal, the generalist or the specialist, would be better adapted for survival in a changing ecosystem? Why?

Generalists would be better adapted to a changing ecosystem, because if one food source disappeared they would have other sources of food. A specialist would not be able to survive if its main food source disappeared.

Thinking Critically

Answer the questions using complete sentences.

17. **Express Ideas** Explain why many types of plants and animals can live and find niches in an ocean environment.

   With different depths, different amounts of sunlight,

   different temperatures, and different current strengths, the

   ocean provides many different habitats.

18. **Synthesize** Look at the picture of the food web below. Is the snake a producer, an herbivore, an omnivore, or a carnivore? What would happen in this ecosystem if all of the snakes died out?

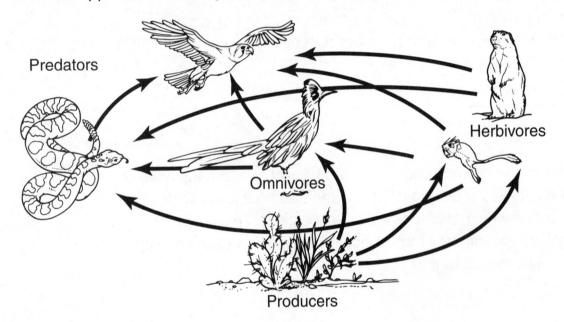

Predators

Herbivores

Omnivores

Producers

   The snake is a carnivore, because it eats birds, small herbivores,

   and no plants. If all of the snakes in the ecosystem died out, then its

   prey, which are birds and small animals, might increase in number.

19. **Analyze** Is the relationship between mosquitoes and humans a parasitic relationship or a predator-prey relationship?

   It is a parasitic relationship because one organism (mosquito)

   is helped and the other organism (human) is harmed.

Chapter Test

Reviewing Vocabulary

Complete each sentence with the correct vocabulary word.

1. A mature ecosystem that remains stable over time is called a(n)
   _____climax community_____.

2. A(n) _____disease_____ is a condition that prevents a
   living thing from functioning properly.

3. Places of great biodiversity that are threatened by human
   activity are known as _____biodiversity hotspots_____.

Circle the letter of the best answer.

4. What process occurs when plant and animal communities
   become established in an area that had no plants or animals
   before?

   A climax community   **B** pioneer species

   C secondary succession   **D** primary succession

5. Which phrase best describes extinction?

   A the emergence of a new species

   B the complete disappearance of a species

   C the destruction of the habitat of a species

   D the disappearance of one population of a species

Answer the questions using complete sentences.

6. What is a pioneer species?

   A pioneer species is a species that is the first, or one of the

   first, to colonize a particular region of land.

   _____

7. Describe an example of predation that you might see in everyday life.

Possible answers: seagull eating a fish; cat eating a mouse;

bird eating a worm

Checking Main Ideas

**For each statement, circle the word *True* or the word *False*.
Rewrite each false statement to make it true.**

8. Competition for resources occurs only between members of different species.

True   (False)

Competition for resources occurs between members of the same
species as well as between members of different species.

9. Human activities are the only threat to biodiversity on Earth.

True   (False)

In addition to human activities, the invasion of a new area by plants
and animals can also upset the biodiversity of an area.

10. Diseases can affect both plant and animal species.

(True)   False

_____

Circle the letter of the best answer.

11. Which animal species is extinct?

   A rat

   B dodo bird

   C condor

   D Chinese snakehead

12. Which of the following is not usually a limiting factor in population growth?

    A food   **B** water

    C disease   **D** air

Using Inquiry Skills

Answer the questions using complete sentences.

13. Infer A new species is introduced to an ecosystem and competes for the same resources as the native species. Tell what might happen.

Competition for resources will increase. This could lead to

smaller populations of the introduced species or the native species,

depending on which is better at competing for the resource.

14. Analyze Data The graph shows the populations of rabbit and lynx in an ecosystem. What kind of relationship do these species have?

The lynx and the rabbit have a predator–prey relationship.

_____

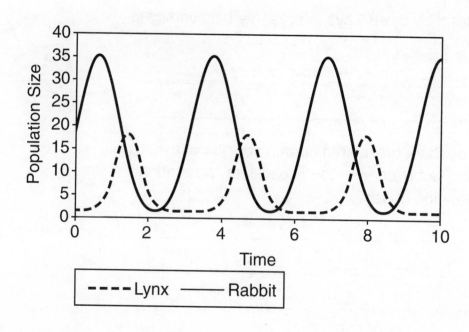

15. **Predict** Due to a volcanic eruption, a region is covered with hot lava and ash. All plant and animal life in the region is destroyed. Describe the ecological process that will take place in this area as time passes.

The first thing to happen will be primary succession, in which pioneer species colonize the area. This will provide new habitats that invite more species. Eventually, the ecosystem will become stable and become a climax community.

Thinking Critically
Answer the questions using complete sentences.

16. **Generate Ideas** Consider a species of bird that lives in a rain forest in South America. The bird eats insects and builds its nests in trees. Describe three things that could make this species of bird become extinct.

The bird's food source could disappear; its habitat could be destroyed; another animal that has the same niche could be introduced into the area and out-compete the bird for resources.

17. **Express Ideas** Describe three ways to preserve biodiversity in the world.

Create nature preserves; limit or stop pollution; limit or stop the destruction of habitats.

18. **Apply** A species of shark preys on a certain species of fish. If that shark species is removed from the ecosystem, what might happen to the population of fish?

Without any predators, the fish population probably would grow until it reached the carrying capacity of the ecosystem. Once it reached the carrying capacity, the fish population would no longer grow, because it would be in balance with the resources of the ecosystem.

Chapter Test

Reviewing Vocabulary

Complete each sentence with the correct vocabulary word.

1. _____Metamorphic_____ rock is formed when existing rock is altered by conditions of extreme pressure and temperature.

2. The measure of how easily a mineral can be scratched is called _____hardness_____.

3. In the _____rock cycle_____, certain types of rock are changed into other types of rock.

Circle the letter of the best answer.

4. Which type of rock is formed from the cooling and hardening of molten rock?

   A igneous rock

   B sedimentary rock

   C metamorphic rock

   D sheet rock

5. Which property describes the way that the surface of a mineral reflects light?

   A hardness

   B cleavage

   C luster

   D streak

Answer the questions using complete sentences.

6. What term describes the property of breaking along flat surfaces?

   The property is called cleavage.
   _____

7. Which type of rock is formed from the compacting of sediments?

Sedimentary rock is formed when sediments are compacted.

8. What are the solid compounds that occur in Earth's crust called?

The solid compounds are called minerals.

Checking Main Ideas

For each statement, circle the word *True* or the word *False*. Rewrite each false statement to make it true.

9. Metamorphic rock can form only from igneous rock that has been exposed to high temperature and pressure.

True (False)

Metamorphic rock can form from igneous, sedimentary, or other metamorphic rock.

10. Some minerals are soft and malleable, while others are very hard.

(True) False

_____

11. Sedimentary rock is the only type of rock that is broken down by weathering and erosion.

True (False)

All three types of rock, sedimentary, metamorphic, and igneous, are broken down by weathering and erosion.

Circle the letter of the best answer.

12. Which quality of diamond gives it its unusual hardness?

   A the fact that it is made up of only oxygen atoms

   B the fact that it is made up of only carbon atoms

   C the fact that its carbon atoms are arranged in sheets

   (D) the fact that each carbon atom is bound to four other carbon atoms in a stable structure

13. The rock here can be classified as

A   sedimentary rock

B   igneous rock

C   metamorphic rock

D   compacted rock

14. Quartz is used in the manufacture of

A   wallboard

B   copper wire

C   soap

D   watches and clocks

Using Inquiry Skills

Answer the questions using complete sentences.

15. Use Numbers An unknown mineral scratches quartz, which has a hardness of 7. Topaz, with a hardnes of 8, is capable of scratching this unknown mineral. What is the approximate hardness of this unknown mineral?

The hardness of this unknown mineral is between 7 and 8.

16. Observe You are walking near a volcanic mountain range. You pick up a piece of rock and notice that it is surprisingly light, and tan in color. What type of rock is this most likely to be?

Because this rock was found near a volcanic mountain range, it might be igneous rock. It is surprisingly light, and has a tan color, so it could be the igneous rock known as pumice.

17. Compare How are sedimentary rock and igneous rock formed? Compare the two processes.

Sedimentary rock is formed when layers of sediments pile

up. The weight of the layers of rock squeezes out the water

and compacts the sediments into stone. Igneous rock is

formed when molten rock cools and hardens.

Thinking Critically

Answer the questions using complete sentences.

18. Analyze While walking near an ocean beach, you find a large rock face that has layers of different types of minerals in it. As you get closer, you notice that there are tiny shells embedded in the layers. What can you infer about the history of this rock?

This rock was probably formed under

the ocean. At some point, the rock was

uplifted during some geological event.

Chapter Test

Reviewing Vocabulary

Complete each sentence with the correct vocabulary word.

1. Earth's crust is broken up into irregularly shaped sections called
   _____tectonic plates_____.

2. The point on Earth's surface directly above the focus of an
   earthquake is called the _____epicenter_____.

3. The _____crust_____ is the thin, outer layer of Earth, of
   which the continents are a part.

Circle the letter of the best answer.

4. The thin layers of sediment shown in this
   picture are called

   A tectonic plates

   B stripes

   C strata

   D mantle

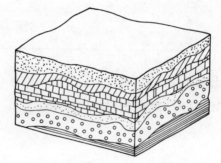

5. Huge ocean waves caused by earthquakes are called

   A hurricanes

   B tsunamis

   C tornados

   D storms

Answer the questions using complete sentences.

6. What is the name of the point directly below the epicenter where
   an earthquake begins?

   An earthquake begins at a point known as the focus.

   _____

7. What is another name for earthquake vibrations?

Earthquake vibrations are called seismic waves. _____

_____

8. Which Earth layer is located just beneath the crust?

The Earth layer just below the crust is called the mantle. _____

_____

Checking Main Ideas

For each statement, circle the word *True* or the word *False*. Rewrite each false statement to make it true.

9. Only animals with hard body parts can create fossils.

True   (False)

Animals with soft body parts can create fossils by leaving behind imprints of their bodies.

10. All of the continents of Earth were once part of one large landmass known as Pangaea.

(True)   False

_____

11. Convergent boundaries occur where plates are moving apart.

True   (False)

Convergent boundaries occur where plates are moving toward each other.

Circle the letter of the best answer.

12. Which earthquake waves are the fastest?

   (A) P-waves

   B S-waves

   C L-waves

   D M-waves

13. What is one way of determining the age of a fossil?

    A through the size of the fossil

    B through the strata of rock in which it is found

    C through the temperature of the fossil

    D through the weight of the fossil

Using Inquiry Skills
Answer the questions using complete sentences.

14. Infer Fossil A is found in a horizontal layer of rock. Fossil B is found in a horizontal layer of rock below Fossil A. What can you infer about the relative ages of these fossils?

Because Fossil B was found in a layer below Fossil A, it is probably older than Fossil A.

15. Compare Compare the movement of plates at convergent boundaries, divergent boundaries, and transform fault boundaries.

Convergent boundaries are boundaries where plates are pushing together. Divergent boundaries are boundaries where plates are moving away from each other. Transform fault boundaries are places where plates are sliding past one another.

Thinking Critically

Answer the questions using complete sentences.

16. Apply Why are earthquakes common along transform fault boundaries?

Earthquakes are common along transform fault boundaries because the plates are sliding by each other. Plates do not have smooth edges so as they move they "stick." When enough pressure builds up the rock can suddenly move causing an earthquake.

17. Synthesize New Zealand is located at the boundary of the Australian Plate and the Pacific Plate. The Australian plate is moving north, while the Pacific plate is moving west. What kind of geographic features and natural disasters do you think are common in New Zealand?

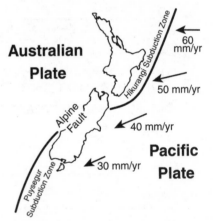

The fact that New Zealand is located on a plate boundary is probably the reason for many natural disasters such as earthquakes and volcanic eruptions. I would also expect that, over time, the collision of these two plates has created large mountain ranges in this country.

Chapter Test

Reviewing Vocabulary

Complete each sentence with the correct vocabulary word.

1. ___Fossil fuels___, such as petroleum, coal, and oil, formed from ancient plants and animals.

2. Resources that can be replenished are known as ___renewable resources___.

3. ___Solar energy___ is energy from the Sun.

Circle the letter of the best answer.

4. Which is nonliving matter that could potentially be used for fuel?
   - **A** biomass
   - **B** hybrid
   - **C** electricity
   - **D** solar

5. What is electrical energy generated from moving water called?
   - **A** geothermal energy
   - **B** solar energy
   - **C** biomass energy
   - **D** hydroelectric energy

Answer the questions using complete sentences.

6. What form of energy involves the use of radioactive material?

   Nuclear energy is a form of energy that involves the use of radioactive material, like uranium.

7. What is the source of geothermal energy?

The source of geothermal energy is heat from Earth's

interior.

8. What are natural resources that cannot be replenished called?

Resources that can't be replenished are called

nonrenewable resources.

Checking Main Ideas

For each statement, circle the word *True* or the word *False*. Rewrite each false statement to make it true.

9. Solar energy was first used in the 21st century.

True   (False)

Solar energy was used in the late 1800s and early 1900s.

10. Nuclear energy can be harnessed without harm to the environment.

True   (False)

Nuclear energy is potentially harmful to the environment.

11. Most of the energy used in the United States comes from renewable sources.

True   (False)

Most of the energy used in the United States comes from fossil fuels, which are nonrenewable resources.

Circle the letter of the best answer.

12. Fossil fuels were primarily formed during the

    A Cambrian period

    B Cretaceous period

    (**C**) Carboniferous period

    D pre-Cambrian period

13. The object shown here is used to harness energy from

   A the Sun

   B wind

   C water

   D radioactive material

14. Which statement describes a possible way to decrease the amount of petroleum used in the United States?

   A switch all of the heating systems of houses to electric heating

   B switch all of the heating systems of houses to solar heating

   B change all of the stoves to electric stoves

   C convert all of the cars to cars with electric motors

Using Inquiry Skills

Answer the questions using complete sentences.

15. **Infer** Suppose all of the cars that now use petroleum for energy were converted to use hydrogen for energy. What effect might this have on the environment?

   If all of the cars that now use petroleum were converted to

   hydrogen-using cars, air would be cleaner because there

   would be less burning of fossil fuels.

16. **Hypothesize** Why are fossil fuels classified as nonrenewable resources?

   Fossil fuels are nonrenewable because they take millions of

   years to form.

Thinking Critically

Answer the questions using complete sentences.

17. **Solve Problems** Describe three ways that you can help conserve fossil fuels on a daily basis.

Answers may vary. One way to conserve fossil fuels is to use
less electricity. Another way is to take public transportation,
which reduces the number of cars on the road. A third way is
by recycling, because it takes less energy to make products
from recycled materials than it does to make them new.

18. **Synthesize** Describe two different ways that people now use renewable resources to create energy.

People can use wind turbines to create electricity. They
can build dams to create hydroelectric energy. They can
use heat from Earth's interior to provide geothermal energy.
They can use solar panels to trap solar energy.

Chapter Test

Reviewing Vocabulary

Complete each sentence with the correct vocabulary word.

1. Rain, snow, hail, and sleet are types of ___precipitation___.

2. A funnel-shaped cloud with rapidly rotating winds is a ___tornado___.

3. Average weather conditions over a long period of time describe the ___climate___ of an area.

4. The ___Coriolis effect___ causes winds to curve to the left in the Southern Hemisphere.

5. A loop of rising and sinking air or water caused by differences in density is a ___convection current___.

6. A continuous moving stream of water of similar temperature and density is a(n) ___ocean current___.

7. A(n) ___jet stream___ is a belt of high-speed winds in the troposphere.

8. A(n) ___air mass___ is a large body of air.

9. Two air masses meet along a boundary, or ___front___.

10. A(n) ___thunderstorm___ is a small, intense weather system that generates heavy rain and strong winds.

Name _____ Date _____

Checking Main Ideas

For each statement, circle the word *True* or the word *False*.
Rewrite each false statement to make it true.

11. A front is the boundary where two ocean currents meet.

   True   (False)

   A front is the boundary where two air masses meet.

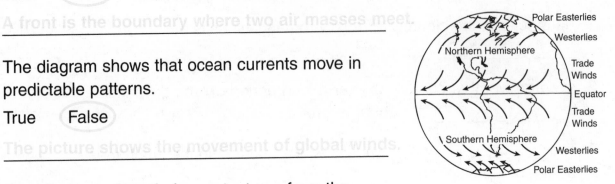

12. The diagram shows that ocean currents move in predictable patterns.

   True   (False)

   The picture shows the movement of global winds.

13. Earth's atmosphere helps protect you from the Sun's harmful radiation.

   (True)   False

14. Thunderstorms form when cool, dry air is pushed upward at a front.

   True   (False)

   Thunderstorms form when warm, moist air is pushed upward at a front.

Using Inquiry Skills

Answer the questions using complete sentences.

15. Classify Name each type of front.

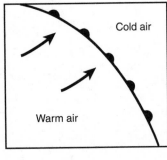 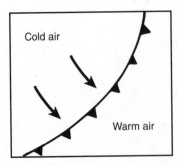

   warm front   cold front

16. Compare How is Earth's atmosphere like a greenhouse?

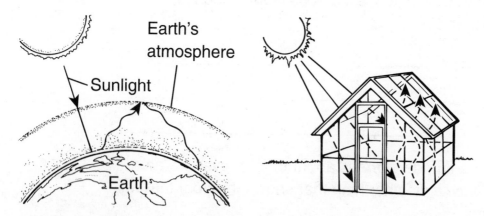

Energy from the Sun warms the Earth and its atmosphere

much like it warms a greenhouse. Like the glass panels of a

greenhouse, gases in the atmosphere trap solar radiation.

17. Predict How might removing the glass panels of a greenhouse affect the plants inside?

The temperature inside the greenhouse would change with

the outside weather conditions. The plants might not survive.

Thinking Critically

Answer the questions using complete sentences.

18. Generate Ideas How does sunscreen prevent ultraviolet radiation from burning your skin? Generate as many ideas as you can.

Possible answers: Sunscreen reflects ultraviolet radiation away from your

skin. Sunscreen absorbs ultraviolet radiation before it reaches your skin.

The sunscreen forms a barrier to the passage of ultraviolet radiation.

19. Draw Conclusions How would a jet stream affect an airliner flying through it from east to west across North America? Explain your answer.

The jet stream would slow down the airliner. Jet streams are located in the upper levels of the troposphere where aircraft pass through. They move from west to east across North America and produce high-speed winds.

20. Apply Imagine a thunderstorm is about to form over the area shown below. Draw a weather map that shows the front that will create the storm. Students should draw a warm front using half-circles facing the direction in which the front is moving.

Chapter Test

Reviewing Vocabulary

Complete each sentence with the correct vocabulary word.

1. The daily changes in the ocean level at shorelines around the world are called _____tides_____.

2. The different shapes of the Moon's appearance are called _____phases_____.

3. Earth makes a full _____rotation_____ in one day.

4. During a _____neap tide_____ the Sun and the Moon pull on Earth's oceans from different directions.

Match each vocabulary word to its description.

5. lunar eclipse   an orbit around the Sun

6. solar eclipse   Moon passes through Earth's shadow

7. revolution   Moon casts a shadow on Earth

Checking Main Ideas

For each statement, circle the word *True* or the word *False*. Rewrite each false statement to make it true.

8. The Moon is the only space object that causes tides on Earth.

    True   (False)

    The Moon and Sun both cause tides.

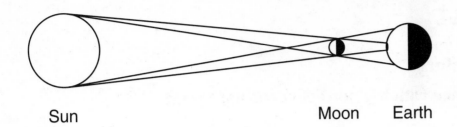

Sun   Moon   Earth

9. The picture above shows a lunar eclipse.

True   (False)

The picture shows a solar eclipse.
_____

10. Virtually all of the energy need to sustain life on Earth is provided by the Sun.

(True)   False

_____

11. Earth's rotation causes the seasons to change.

True   (False)

Earth's revolution around the Sun and the tilt of Earth's

axis cause the seasons to change.
_____

Circle the letter of the correct answer.

12. Which of the following is true?

   A Both the Moon and the Sun orbit Earth.

   (B) The Moon orbits Earth and Earth orbits the Sun.

   C The Sun orbits the Moon and Earth orbits the Sun.

   D The Moon orbits the Sun and Earth orbits the Sun.

13. The Sun is

   A the least massive body in the solar system

   B made mostly of helium

   (C) the largest and most massive body in the solar system

   D a huge sphere of very cold plasma

Using Inquiry Skills

Answer the questions using complete sentences.

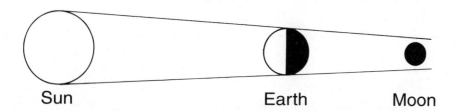

Sun   Earth   Moon

14. Infer What kind of eclipse is occurring in the picture above?

The picture shows a lunar eclipse.

15. Predict What would happen to the seasons if Earth's axis of rotation was not tilted? Why?

There would be no seasons at all, because each part of Earth

would receive the same amount of sunlight all year.

16. Use Models How could you use a light, your hand, and your head to model solar and lunar eclipses?

The light could represent the Sun, my head could

represent Earth, and my hand could represent the

Moon. I could use my hand to block the light so it could

cast a shadow on my face. This would model a solar

eclipse. To model a lunar eclipse, I could block the light

with my head so it could cast a shadow on my hand.

17. Hypothesize Suppose Earth had a much more massive Moon. How might this affect tides on Earth?

If the Moon was much more massive, it would exert much more

gravitational pull on the Earth's oceans producing higher tides.

Thinking Critically

Answer the questions using complete sentences.

18. Solve Problems Suppose you were lost in the woods. How could you use the Sun to find your way out?

The Sun moves across the sky from east to south to west.

Given the time of day, you can use the position of the Sun

to tell direction.

19. Synthesize Why do solar eclipses only occur during the new moon phase?

A solar eclipse occurs when the Moon is directly between Earth

and the Sun. At that time, only the side of the Moon away from

Earth is lit, which is the new moon phase.

Chapter Test

Reviewing Vocabulary

Complete each sentence with the correct vocabulary word.

1. An instrument that gathers light to form an enlarged image of a distant object is a(n) ____optical telescope____.

2. An irregularly shaped object that orbits the Sun, often found in a belt between Mars and Jupiter, is a(n) ____asteroid____.

3. The brightness of a star as it appears to an observer on Earth is its ____apparent magnitude____.

4. A frozen ball of ice and rock that has an irregular orbit around the Sun is called a(n) ____comet____.

5. The distance that light travels in a year is a(n) ____light-year____.

6. Scientists describe distances in our solar system in terms of the ____astronomical unit____, which equals the average distance from Earth to the Sun.

7. The measure of how much light a star actually gives off is its ____absolute magnitude____.

8. All stars form from a rotating cloud of gas and dust, composed mainly of hydrogen, called a(n) ____nebula____.

9. Our local star, the Sun, is only one of billions of stars belonging to a(n) ____galaxy____ called the Milky Way.

10. A small rocky object that is bumped from its orbit becomes a(n) ____meteoroid____.

Checking Main Ideas

Answer the questions using complete sentences.

11. Name the inner planets. What characteristics do they share?

The inner planets are Mercury, Venus, Earth, and Mars. All of the inner

planets are solid bodies, similar in composition to Earth.

12. Why do the planets remain in orbit around the Sun?

The Sun exerts a strong gravitational pull on the planets.

13. Give two reasons why some stars appear brighter than others.

Some stars appear brighter because they are relatively

close to Earth. Other stars appear brighter because they

are hotter or bigger and give off more light.

14. What type of galaxy is shown in the picture? Label the three
main parts of this galaxy.

The galaxy is a spiral galaxy. Students should label the

bulge, the halo, and the disk.

Name _____ Date _____

Using Inquiry Skills

Answer the questions using complete sentences.

The Hertzsprung-Russell Diagram

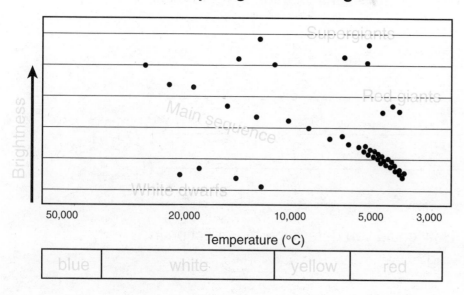

15. **Communicate** Besides temperature, what feature of stars does the Hertzsprung-Russell Diagram compare? Label this feature on the vertical axis.

16. **Use Models** How do the colors of stars change with temperature? Record the star color at each temperature level in the boxes below the H-R diagram.

17. **Classify** Label the four different types of stars on the H-R diagram.

Thinking Critically

Answer the questions using complete sentences.

18. **Compare** How does Pluto compare with the other outer planets? Why do you think some scientists think that Pluto is not a planet?

The other outer planets are gas giants, much larger in size

than tiny Pluto. They have thick atmospheres, rings, many

moons, and are composed mainly of gases. Pluto is similar in

composition to some of the moons of these giant planets. It

may even be a moon of Neptune that was thrown out of orbit.

19. **Draw Conclusions** How could you determine the direction in which a comet is moving?

A comet's tail always points away from the Sun. When the comet

is moving toward the inner part of the solar system, its tail flows

behind the comet. When it is leaving the inner solar system,

the comet tail would be pointing in front of the comet.

20. **Analyze** Why is it that the Sun is the brightest star in the sky, even though it is not the largest?

The Sun is a medium-sized star, but it appears to be bright

because it is very close to Earth, compared to the other

stars.

Chapter Test

Reviewing Vocabulary

Complete each sentence with the correct vocabulary word.

1. The particle inside the nucleus of an atom that has no charge is called a(n) _____neutron_____.

2. A pure substance that cannot be broken down into simpler substances is a(n) _____element_____.

3. Negatively charged particles that surround the nucleus of an atom are called _____electrons_____.

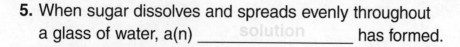

4. If an atom has more electrons than protons, it is a negatively charged _____ion_____.

5. When sugar dissolves and spreads evenly throughout a glass of water, a(n) _____solution_____ has formed.

6. Lemon juice, with its sour taste and a pH of 2, is a(n) _____acid_____.

Checking Main Ideas

Circle the letter of the best answer.

7. The three particles that make up atoms are
    A protons, ions, and neutrons
    B neutrons, electrons, and isotopes
    C protons, neutrons, and bonds
    D protons, neutrons, and electrons

8. The smallest unit of an element, known as the basic building block of matter, is the

    A electron

    B atom

    C nucleus

    D ion

9. Elements in today's periodic table are arranged according to

    A date of discovery

    B atomic mass

    C density

    D atomic number

10. Which substance is a mixture?

    A chicken noodle soup

    B pure water

    C oxygen

    D carbon dioxide

11. Which is NOT a characteristic of a base?

    A slippery feel

    B low concentration of hydrogen ions

    C does not react easily with other substances

    D bitter taste

12. A safe way to find out if a substance is an acid is to

    A taste it

    B mix it with water

    C heat it slowly until it boils

    D dip litmus paper into it and look for a color change

Assessment Resources

Name _____ Date _____

**For each statement, circle the word *True* or the word *False*.
Rewrite each false statement to make it true.**

13. The household objects shown in this picture are
    examples of acids.

    True   (False)

    The household objects are examples

    of bases.

14. All matter can be divided into three major groups: pure
    substances, mixtures, and compounds.

    True   (False)

    Matter can be divided into two major groups: pure

    substances and mixtures.

Using Inquiry Skills

Use a complete Periodic Table to answer the questions.

15. **Analyze Data** The chemical formula of common table salt
    is NaCl. What are the names of the elements that form this
    compound?

    sodium, chlorine

16. **Compare** Write the name of an element that has properties in
    common with oxygen.

    choice of sulfur, selenium, tellurium, or polonium

17. **Communicate** Write the chemical symbol for gold.

    Au

18. **Use Numbers** Write the number of protons in an atom of nickel.

    28

Thinking Critically

Answer the questions using complete sentences.

19. **Solve Problems** What could you do if you needed to quickly dissolve a lot of salt in a container of water?

The water could be stirred and heated while the salt is

being added.

20. **Apply** When people get stomach pains, it is sometimes because the stomach is overproducing stomach acid. Stomach acid has a pH of 1. Antacids are bases that people take to ease the discomfort caused by stomach acids. In terms of pH, describe how an antacid might work.

The antacid, which is a base, neutralizes the stomach acid.

The antacid helps bring the pH of the stomach contents

closer to pH 7, which is neutral.

Chapter Test

Reviewing Vocabulary

Complete each sentence with the correct vocabulary word.

1. The amount of space that a substance fills is its
   _____volume_____.

2. A measure of the average energy that results from the motion of particles in a substance is called _____temperature_____.

3. The change in matter shown in the picture is an example of a _____chemical_____ change.

4. At a substance's _____boiling point_____, liquid turns to gas.

5. During photosynthesis, the energy of sunlight is absorbed. Therefore, photosynthesis is classified as a(n) _____endothermic_____ chemical reaction.

6. The law of _____conservation of matter_____ states that matter cannot be created or destroyed.

Checking Main Ideas

For each statement, circle the word _True_ or the word _False_. Rewrite each false statement to make it true.

7. When matter undergoes a physical change, its chemical makeup changes.

   True (False)

   _____When matter undergoes a physical change, its chemical_____

   _____makeup remains the same._____

8. An example of an endothermic reaction is shown in the picture.

True   (False)

Fireworks are an example of an exothermic reaction.

_____

9. In a chemical change, existing bonds break and new bonds form, but matter is neither created nor destroyed.

(True)   False

_____

_____

10. When a substance, such as water, is frozen its particles stop moving.

True   (False)

Particles in solid and frozen substances are always moving.

They just move less.

11. The graph shows that, at a constant pressure, the temperature of gas decreases as its volume increases.

True   (False)

The graph shows that volume increases

as temperature increases.

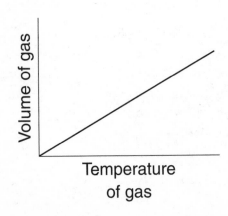

Volume of gas

Temperature
of gas

Circle the correct answer.

12. The melting point of a substance occurs at the same temperature as its _____.

(freezing point)   boiling point   point of condensation

13. Which must change in order for a substance to transform from a gas to a liquid?

(temperature)   pressure   volume

14. Which is not a type of chemical reaction?

synthesis   decomposition   (vaporization)

Using Inquiry Skills

Answer the questions using complete sentences.

15. **Compare** Which would have more volume—one pound of hot food fresh off the stove, or one pound of the same leftover food in the refrigerator? Why?

The hot food would have more volume, because, in general, substances expand when heated and contract when cooled.

16. **Predict** You pump air into a basketball using a bicycle pump. Predict the changes in gas pressure inside the basketball. Why does this happen?

The pressure of the air increases because more air molecules are in the basketball.

17. Observe A marshmallow is cooked over an open flame. What observable clue tells you that the marshmallow is undergoing a chemical change?

Before   After

The outer surface of the
_____

marshmallow has changed color.
_____

_____

18. Classify Which type of chemical reaction is a campfire— endothermic or exothermic? Why?

It is exothermic because it gives off heat and light.
_____

Thinking Critically

Answer the questions using complete sentences.

19. Apply The equation for the decomposition of water is shown below:

$$2 H_2O \rightarrow 2 H_2 + O_2$$

How does this equation illustrate how matter is conserved during a chemical reaction?

According to the law of conservation of matter, the total mass of the
_____

substances in a chemical reaction does not change, no matter what
_____

new products form. In this reaction, there are four hydrogen atoms
_____

and two oxygen atoms on each side of the arrow.
_____

20. Synthesize A firefly makes light in its body without electricity. Describe what must be happening inside the firefly's body to make this light.

Answers may vary. The firefly creates light through a
_____

chemical reaction, similar to the way a glow stick gives off
_____

light.
_____

Name _____ Date _____

Chapter Test

Reviewing Vocabulary

Match each definition to the correct vocabulary word.

1. A unit used to measure energy and work   amplitude

2. In a wave the distance from the rest position to the crest or trough   joule

3. The distance between a given point on one wave and the same point on the next wave   insulator

4. The transfer of thermal energy by mass movement of particles in a liquid or gas   wavelength

          convection

5. A material that conducts thermal energy poorly

Complete each sentence with the correct vocabulary word.

6. A sound's pitch is related to its _____frequency_____.

7. When this climber rappels down the cliff, some potential energy is converted into _____kinetic energy_____.

8. In a _____fusion_____ reaction, small nuclei join to form new nuclei and large amounts of energy are released.

9. A disturbance that travels from one location to another is known as a _____wave_____.

10. In a _____longitudinal_____ wave, the motion of the particles in the medium is back and forth in the direction the wave travels.

Checking Main Ideas

Circle the letter of the best answer.

11. Which is NOT a type of energy?

   A chemical

   B mechanical

   C electrical

   D longitudinal

12. Flexible objects such as rubber bands have

   A elastic potential energy

   B chemical potential energy

   C elastic kinetic energy

   D potential thermal energy

13. Nuclear power plants use a type of nuclear reaction called

   A fusion

   B fission

   C thermal reaction

   D chemical reaction

14. Sound intensity is measured in units called

   A transverse waves

   B joules

   C decibels

   D hertz

15. The pitch of this police car's siren is high as it approaches and gets lower after it passes. This is an example of

   A the amplitude of sound waves

   B the Doppler effect

   C a transverse wave

   D a longitudinal wave

The pitch of the siren is lower behind the police car.

The pitch of the siren is higher ahead of the police car.

Using Inquiry Skills

Answer the questions using complete sentences.

16. **Compare** Equal masses of three materials—wood, aluminum, and water—are heated. Suppose you measure the temperature of each sample after each has absorbed the same amount of heat. What would you find? Explain.

The aluminum would have the highest temperature,

followed by the wood. The water would have the lowest

temperature. This is because aluminum heats up at a higher

rate than wood, which heats up at a higher rate than water.

17. **Classify** Complete the table using items from the box.

glass jar	gold ring	air	aluminum can
plastic fork	wood spoon	cotton sheet	silver platter
cork	copper penny	wool scarf	salt water

Insulators	Conductors
glass jar	gold ring
air	aluminum can
plastic fork	salt water
wool scarf	copper penny
cotton sheet	silver platter
wood spoon	
cork	

18. Communicate What are the three ways in which thermal energy can be transferred? Give one example of each.

conduction, convection, and radiation. Examples may vary. Conduction: A

metal spoon is placed in a pot of boiling water and heats up. Convection:

Water in a pan is heated. The water at the bottom of the pan expands and

rises to the top. The cooler, denser water at the top sinks to the bottom,

where it is heated. Radiation: Electromagnetic waves from the Sun heat

Earth during the day.

Thinking Critically
Answer the questions using complete sentences.

19. Apply On a hot summer day, the temperature in your living room is 80°F, while the attic temperature is 90°F. Why is the attic hotter than the living room?

The attic may not be insulated as well as the living room.

Also, the attic may be hotter because of convection; hot air

rises.

20. Analyze In archery, a bow and arrow is used to hit a target several feet away. What forms of energy are involved? Describe the transformation from potential energy to kinetic energy.

The bow has elastic potential energy. The archer has potential

chemical energy in his muscles. When the archer pulls back

on the bow the potential chemical energy in his arm muscles

and the potential elastic energy in the bow are transformed into

kinetic energy.

Chapter Test

Reviewing Vocabulary

Answer the questions using complete sentences.

1. What is an electromagnetic wave?

   a wave made up of wave-shaped electric and magnetic fields

   _____

2. What is a translucent material?

   a material that allows some light to pass through it

   _____

3. What is a convex mirror?

   a mirror with a surface that curves out on the shiny side

   _____

4. What is refraction?

   the bending, or changing of direction, of light rays when

   they pass from one material into another

5. What are lasers?

   Answers may vary. Sample responses: devices that produce

   light that only have one color; Laser light is coherent.

**For each statement, circle the word _True_ or the word _False_.
Rewrite each false statement to make it true.**

6. This light bulb is called an incandescent light source.

   (True) False

   _____

7. Opaque material transmits visible light freely.

True   (False)

Opaque material does not transmit visible light.

_____

8. A lens is a transparent material that reflects light to form an image.

True   (False)

A lens is a transparent material that refracts light to form an image.

_____

9. The range of colors that make up visible light is called the visible spectrum.

(True)   False

_____

10. Light waves that are parallel and that have their crests and troughs aligned are known as incoherent light.

True   (False)

Light waves that are parallel and that have their crests and troughs aligned are known as coherent light.

Checking Main Ideas

Circle the letter of the best answer.

11. Which type of electromagnetic radiation carries the least energy?

A gamma rays

(**B**) radio waves

C visible light

D x-rays

12. Eggshells and ivory are examples of materials that are

(**A**) phosphorescent

B bioluminescent

C fluorescent

D incandescent

13. Mirrors like the one this girl is holding

   A cause a diffuse reflection

   B refract light waves

   C are transparent materials

   (D) cause a specular reflection

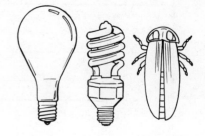

14. A red apple appears red because it

   A refracts only red wavelengths

   B absorbs almost all the light that strikes it

   (C) reflects only red wavelengths

   D refracts almost all the light that strikes it

Using Inquiry Skills

Answer the questions using complete sentences.

15. Predict Suppose these three light sources—fluorescent, phosphorescent, and incandescent—begin emitting light. Predict how their temperatures will change over time. Explain why.

The temperature of the phosphorescent light will increase least rapidly because the light comes from an outside energy source. The temperature of the incandescent light will increase most rapidly because it produces the most heat.

16. Classify Complete the table using the items in the box.

your hand	window glass	frosted window glass	a black car
a wall	red tinted plastic	plane mirror	aluminum foil
a stained glass	a piece of notebook paper	a ream of notebook paper	

Opaque Materials	Translucent Materials	Transparent Materials
your hand	red tinted plastic	window glass
a black car	frosted window glass	
plane mirror	a piece of notebook paper	
aluminum foil	a stained glass	
a wall		
a ream of notebook paper		

Thinking Critically

Answer the questions using complete sentences.

17. Use Models Draw a diagram that shows how the human eye works. Explain the function of each eye part.

The diagram should be similar to the one shown on page F59. The cornea refracts light. The light passes through the pupil. The iris changes the size of the pupil to allow more or less light to enter the eye. The convex lens focuses light to form an image. The image projects on the retina. Rods make it possible to see in dim light; cones make it possible to see colors. The light is converted to electric impulses that are carried to the brain.

Chapter Test

Reviewing Vocabulary

Match each definition to the correct vocabulary word.

1. The continuous flow of electric charges from one place to another

    electricity

2. The movement or interaction of electric charges

    current electricity

3. A circuit in which electrical current flows along a single path

    generator

4. A material that allows electric charges to pass through it easily

    series circuit

5. A device that transforms mechanical energy into electrical energy

    conductor

Complete each sentence with the correct vocabulary word.

6. A magnet is also called a magnetic _____dipole_____ because it has two poles.

7. A(n) _____electric motor_____ is a device that converts electrical energy into mechanical energy.

8. Electric charges do not move easily through a(n) _____insulator_____ .

9. This drawing shows the region around a magnet called the _____magnetic field_____ .

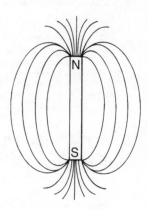

10. A buildup of electrical charges on a material is called _____static electricity_____ .

Checking Main Ideas

Answer the questions using complete sentences.

11. What kind of circuit is this? How does it work?

It is a parallel circuit. In a parallel circuit, current can follow more than one path. When a resistor in one of the paths breaks, current can still flow along the other paths.

12. How do power plants increase or decrease the voltage of electricity?

Power plants use one kind of transformer to increase voltage before sending currents through power lines. At the other end, currents pass through another type of transformer that reduces the voltage.

13. How could you create an electromagnet?

Wrap insulated wire around an iron bar, and send electricity through the wire. The bar becomes a magnet.

14. How does an AC electric motor work?

An insulated wire is coiled around the armature. When current moves through the wire coil, the armature becomes an electromagnet. Attraction and repulsion between the armature's poles and the poles of the permanent magnet cause the armature to rotate.

15. Name three types of data storage systems that are based on magnetic materials.

Sample responses: video and audio recordings, credit cards, ATM cards, computer hard drives

Using Inquiry Skills

Answer the questions using complete sentences.

16. **Predict** On a cold, winter day, you walk across a wool carpet and then touch a metal doorknob. Predict what will happen. Explain why.

    You may feel a small shock because of static electricity.

    Walking on a wool carpet transfers electrons from the

    carpet to your body. You acquire an overall negative charge,

    which will attract positive charges in the doorknob.

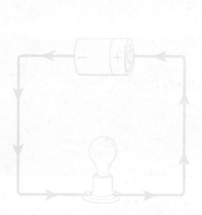

DC current   AC current

17. **Using Models** Draw a simple diagram of an AC current and a DC current. Why do power plants use AC currents?

    With AC currents, transformers can be used to increase or

    decrease the voltage easily and inexpensively.

    _____

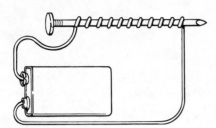

18. Communicate What is shown in the above picture? Explain how it works.

It is an electromagnet. Electricity from the battery flows

through the coiled wire. The nail will remain magnetic as

long as current flows through the wire.

Thinking Critically

Answer the questions using complete sentences.

19. Analyze Why is it dangerous to have electric appliances near you when you are taking a bath?

Water is an excellent conductor of electricity. If an electrical

appliance was dropped into the water, the electricity could

travel from the appliance to your body and electrocute you.

20. Apply What type of circuit should be used for this electrical device?

It should be a parallel circuit because if one bulb broke, the

rest would remain on. Also the bulbs would shine more

brightly than if a series circuit were used.

Chapter Test

Reviewing Vocabulary

Match each definition to the correct vocabulary word.

1. The speed and direction of a moving object

2. Something you choose to compare the motion of all other objects to

3. The tendency of an object at rest to stay at rest

4. The force that opposes the motion of one surface against another

5. A mutually attractive force between objects that have mass

gravity

inertia

friction

velocity

frame of reference

Complete each sentence with the correct vocabulary word.

6. The machine in the picture has an arm that moves around a pivot point called the _____fulcrum_____.

7. _____Speed_____ is a measure of how fast the position of an object changes.

8. The rate at which velocity changes is known as _____acceleration_____.

9. The magnitude of a force is measured in units called _____newtons_____.

10. The pull of gravity on a mass is called its _____weight_____.

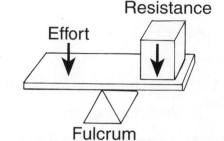

Checking Main Ideas

Circle the letter of the best answer.

11. Average speed can be found using

    A acceleration divided by distance

    B distance divided by time

    C distance divided by velocity

    D mass divided by force

12. What is Newton's third law of motion?

    A Without the action of a force, an object at rest tends to stay at rest.

    B The greater the force, the greater the acceleration.

    C For every action force, there is an equal and opposite reaction force.

    D The greater the mass, the smaller the acceleration.

13. The machines in this picture are examples of

    A first-class levers

    B second-class levers

    C third-class levers

    D a pulley system

14. Gravity is a weak force between two masses unless the masses

    A are very large

    B are moving toward each other

    C are very small

    D are at rest

15. What causes the weightlessness shown in this picture?

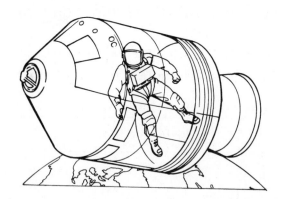

   A The spacecraft is moving at a very high velocity.

   B Earth's gravity is not affecting the astronaut.

   C The spacecraft is at rest.

   D The astronaut and the spacecraft are falling at the same rate.

Using Inquiry Skills

Answer the questions using complete sentences.

16. Compare Can the speeds of these two bicyclists be the same? Can their velocities be the same?

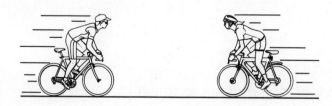

Their speeds can be the same but their velocities cannot, because they are riding in opposite directions.

17. Use Numbers A runner runs 100 meters in 20 seconds. Find the runner's average speed in meters per second. Show your work.

The runner's average speed is 100 m/20 s = 5 m/s.

Thinking Critically

Answer the questions using complete sentences.

18. Predict Who would skate faster, a person using in-line skates on smooth concrete or on grass? Why?

The person skating on smooth concrete would skate faster

because friction between the skates and smooth concrete

is less than friction between the skates and grass.

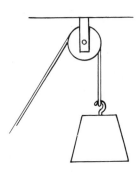  

19. Apply Which simple machine would make it easiest to move a heavy object from the ground to the third floor of a house? Explain why.

The pulley system. It uses many sections of rope to share

the load, so you need a smaller force to lift the object.

20. Analyze You are riding in a car traveling at a speed of 20 mph. A truck traveling at 25 mph in the same direction passes you. Your car stops and a police van passes you going 25 mph. Which vehicle appears to be traveling faster to you? Why?

The police van passing my stopped car appears to move

faster because my frame of reference is different.

Unit Test

Reviewing Vocabulary

Complete each sentence with the correct vocabulary word.

1. Scientists use a ___dichotomous key___ to help classify organisms.

2. A(n) ___allele___ is one form of the gene for a trait.

3. A(n) ___fossil___ is the preserved remains or trace of an organism that lived in the distant past.

4. Small structures in cells that have specific jobs are called ___organelles___.

5. The death of all members of a species is called ___extinction___.

6. Ancient bacteria that live in extreme environments are classified in Kingdom ___Archaebacteria___.

7. When two alleles are both expressed, the inheritance is called ___codominant___.

Checking Main Ideas

For each statement, circle the word *True* or the word *False*. Rewrite each false statement to make it true.

8. A tiger is an example of an invertebrate.

   True   (False)

   ___A tiger is a vertebrate.___

9. Vascular plants that produce flowers are angiosperms.

   (True)   False

   _____

10. Natural selection is the practice in which people choose organisms with desirable traits to reproduce.

True   (False)

Selective breeding is the practice in which people choose organisms with desirable traits to reproduce.

Circle the letter of the best answer.

11. Which organelle captures the energy of sunlight?

   A cytoplasm   **C** vacuole

   B mitochondria   **(D)** chloroplast

12. Which body system helps regulate the amount of water in the blood?

   (A) urinary system   **C** respiratory system

   B immune system   **D** nervous system

13. How many cells remain when a cell finishes the process of meiosis?

   A one   **C** three

   B two   **(D)** four

14. Which structure is homologous to the paw of a cat?

   A the leg of a bird   **(C)** the hand of a human

   B the eye of a bat   **D** the wing of an insect

Using Inquiry Skills

Answer the questions using complete sentences.

15. Ask Questions What questions could be part of a dichotomous key to help classify these two trees?

Are the leaf tips round? Are the leaf tips pointed?

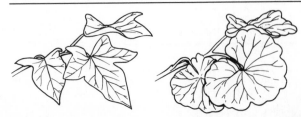

16. Apply What characteristics do these organisms have in common? How do they differ?

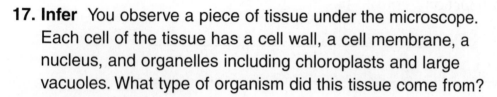

Both are vertebrate, warm-blooded animals. Birds

have feathers, wings, and beaks. Birds lay eggs.

Mammals have hair, give birth to live young, and

feed milk to their young. Mammals have teeth.

17. Infer You observe a piece of tissue under the microscope. Each cell of the tissue has a cell wall, a cell membrane, a nucleus, and organelles including chloroplasts and large vacuoles. What type of organism did this tissue come from?

The tissue came from a plant.

18. Analyze Data The dominant allele for flower color in pea plants is purple (P). The recessive allele is white (p). Out of a generation of 100 pea plants, 31 have alleles PP, 46 have alleles Pp, and 23 have alleles pp. How many of the plants are purple?

77; 31 have PP and 46 have Pp, which makes 77 plants with

allele P.

19. Compare What is the difference between an imprint fossil and a cast fossil?

An imprint fossil is an impression of an organism left in soft mud

that hardens into rock. A cast fossil is a fossil, formed from a

mold, which retains the shape of the original organism.

Thinking Critically

Answer the questions using complete sentences.

20. Evaluate How do fungi differ from plants?

Fungi cannot make their own food. Fungi absorb nutrients

from their environment.

21. Synthesize Explain how the muscular system and the skeletal system work together in the human body.

Muscles are attached to bones. Bones support muscles,

allowing muscles to contract and generate body movements.

22. Analyze What is the difference between sexual reproduction and asexual reproduction?

In sexual reproduction, offspring contain DNA from two parents.

Each organism in every generation gets a unique combination of traits.

In asexual reproduction, only one parent cell or organism produces

offspring. The offspring have the same DNA as the parent.

23. Draw Conclusions Fossils of monkeys, tree frogs, crocodiles, wild pigs, and parrots are discovered in a hot, dry, desert area. What can you conclude about the climate of this area when these organisms were alive?

The area must have had a very different climate, probably a

tropical climate.

24. Synthesize Charles Darwin produced different varieties of pigeons by selectively breeding them. How do you think this work helped Darwin develop the idea of natural selection?

By choosing pigeons with desirable traits and allowing them to

reproduce, Darwin observed that he could produce different

varieties of pigeons. This work gave Darwin the idea that a similar

process, natural selection, might also take place in nature.

Name _____ Date _____

Organizing Concepts

25. Complete the concept map below.

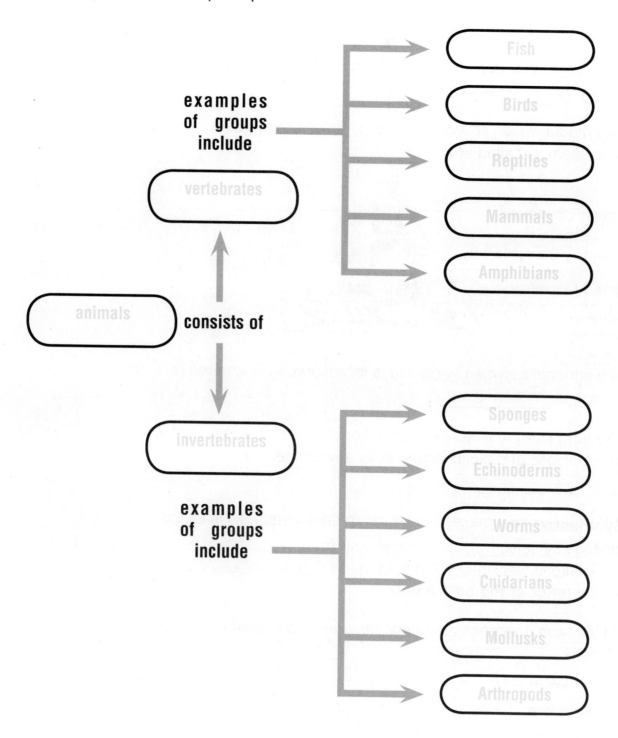

Name _____ Date _____

Unit Test

Reviewing Vocabulary

Complete each sentence with the correct vocabulary word.

1. Consumers that get their energy from eating only meat are known as ____carnivores____.

2. This model, which shows how energy moves through an ecosystem, is called a(n) ____energy pyramid____.

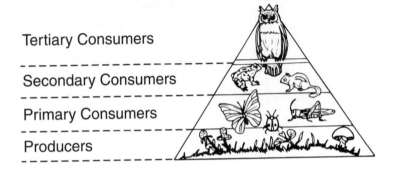

Tertiary Consumers

Secondary Consumers

Primary Consumers

Producers

3. The struggle between living things for resources in an area is known as ____competition____.

4. The term used to describe the relationship of a species to the abiotic and biotic factors in its environment is ____niche____.

5. An organism that makes food through photosynthesis is called a(n) ____producer____.

Circle the letter of the best answer.

6. Which term describes an animal that eats many different kinds of food?

   A omnivore

   B herbivore

   C carnivore

   D prey

7. Which phrase describes a secondary consumer?

   A an organism that eats only plants

   B an organism that eats only animals

   C an organism that makes food through photosynthesis

   D an organism that eats both plants and animals

Checking Main Ideas

Answer the questions using complete sentences.

8. Are limiting resources usually abiotic factors, biotic factors, or both?

Limiting resources are usually things like air, food, water,

and space. Some of those things are abiotic, like water and

air, and some are biotic, like food.

9. What type of ecological succession occurs after a natural disruption such as an earthquake or volcano?

Primary succession; In primary succession, pioneer

species enter the area and make it livable for other species.

Over time, different communities develop resulting in a

stable climax community.

10. Considering that 75% of Earth's surface is covered with water, why is water conservation important?

Most of Earth's water is salt water and is not drinkable.

Less than 1% of the world's water is usable fresh water.

11. Are all symbiotic relationships either beneficial or harmless to its organisms? Explain your answer.

Some symbiotic relationships are beneficial to one or more of the

organisms involved in them. These types of relationships are known as

mutualism and commensalism. A symbiotic relationship involving an

organism that is harmed is known as parasitism.

12. Which is NOT a way that organisms interact within a ecosystem?

A predation

B competition

C symbiotic relationships

D hibernation

13. Which substance cycles through the environment, is necessary for plant growth, and is "fixed" by bacteria that live among the roots of plants?

A nitrogen

B oxygen

C carbon dioxide

D water

14. A population that is stressed by overcrowding and that has a lack of food and water would be most susceptible to

A an invasive species

B disease

C primary succession

D competition

15. Comparing Compare the way oxygen cycles through the biosphere with the way nitrogen cycles through the biosphere.

Oxygen is produced by plants during photosynthesis and during the

breakdown of dead plants and animals by decomposers. Oxygen

is consumed by animals during respiration. Nitrogen exists in the

atmosphere, and is "fixed" into a form that can be used by plants. Nitrogen

is taken up by plant roots and consumed by animals when they eat the

plants. When these animals die decomposers break down their remains,

releasing nitrogen back into the soil and air.

16. **Infer** A new species of animal is discovered. The animal has four legs, can run at speeds up to 30 miles per hour for short periods of time, and has sharp teeth. Is this animal an herbivore, omnivore, or carnivore? Why?

Two facts suggest that the animal is a carnivore. First, it can run quickly, which a carnivore needs to capture its prey. It also has sharp teeth, which carnivores need for eating meat.

Thinking Critically

Answer the questions using complete sentences.

17. **Compare** How are producers and primary consumers on land similar to and different from producers and primary consumers in the ocean?

On land, the producers are trees and other plants. The primary consumers are herbivores and omnivores such as birds, animals, and insects, which all include plants in their diet. In the ocean, the producers are algae, and the primary consumers are herring and other types of smaller fish that eat the algae.

18. **Generate Ideas** Kudzu is a vine-like plant that is found in many parts of the United States. It is an invasive plant species that grows very rapidly and is very hardy. Now people are trying to get rid of it. Explain why.

Invasive species are harmful because they can destroy the balance of ecosystems. A hardy and fast-growing plant could compete with native plants for the resources of an ecosystem. This might limit the amount of space, light, or air for the native species, which could die out.

Organizing Concepts

19. Complete the organizer. Summarize the steps of ecological
succession.

Ecological Succession

Primary Succession
Communities of plants and animals are established
where no organisms exist. Pioneer species are the first
to colonize the land.

Secondary Succession
Fire, landslides, floods, or hurricanes destroy stable
ecosystems. Pioneer species are usually fast-growing
grasses and weeds. Slower-growing and taller plants
arrive, followed by small trees. Larger trees develop,
providing new habitats for more species.

Climax Community
Over time, the community of plants and animals
reaches a fairly stable state. Change is slow, until a
new disturbance hits.

Unit Test

Reviewing Vocabulary

Complete each sentence with the correct vocabulary word.

1. When a mineral is rubbed against a rough surface, it can leave a mark called a _____streak_____.

2. _____Sea-floor spreading_____ occurs when two plates that form a mid-oceanic ridge move apart.

3. The places where Earth's tectonic plates meet are called _____plate boundaries_____.

4. A _____fossil_____ is the remains or traces of an organism that lived in the distant past.

5. The crust and the upper part of the mantle form a rocky layer called the _____lithosphere_____.

Circle the letter of the best answer.

6. Energy that is captured from Earth's hot interior is called

   A nuclear energy

   B geothermal energy

   C solar energy

   D hydroelectric energy

7. Sandstone is classified as

   A sedimentary rock

   B igneous rock

   C metamorphic rock

   D stratified rock

Checking Main Ideas

Answer the questions using complete sentences.

8. What are some things that scientists can learn from studying fossils?

   From studying fossils, scientists can learn about the history

   of life on Earth. They can learn how life has changed over

   time. They can learn what Earth's climate was like in the past.

9. On what basis do scientists classify rocks?

   Rocks are classified by how they are formed.

10. On which Earth layer do tectonic plates move?

   The tectonic plates move on the layer of the mantle that is

   just below the lithosphere. This layer of the mantle is made up of

   denser melted rock, which is what enables the plates to float.

11. What causes a volcanic eruption?

   A volcanic eruption occurs when magma is forced up to

   Earth's surface through an opening in the crust.

Circle the letter of the best answer.

12. The two smaller continents that were formed when Pangaea broke up were called

   A Gondwanaland and Laurasia

   B Gondwanaland and Asialand

   C Laurasia and Asialand

   D Laurasia and Gondwania

13. The layer indicated by the X in the picture is known as what?

    A inner core

    B outer core

    C mantle

    D crust

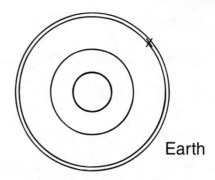

Earth

Using Inquiry Skills

Answer the questions using complete sentences.

14. Infer You are hiking in the Appalachian Mountains and find a large rock with multicolored layers and curving folds. What type of rock could this be? How did this rock most likely form?

This is probably a metamorphic rock because it has both

layers and folds. Metamorphic rocks form when sedimentary,

igneous, and other metamorphic rocks are exposed to high

temperatures and pressures. The high pressure causes

the minerals to arrange themselves in layers.

15. Compare In which environment are fossils most likely to form; a hot, wet environment or a cold, dry environment? Why?

Fossils are most likely to form in the cold, dry environment,

because the remains of the animal or plant are not likely to

decompose quickly, as they would in the hot, wet environment.

16. Infer How was this landscape region likely produced?

Mountains are usually created at convergent plate boundaries

where plates are pushing together. The edges of the plates

crumple, forming mountains.

Thinking Critically

Answer the questions using complete sentences.

17. Analyze The city of London, England, is on the Eurasian plate. The Eurasian plate is moving at a rate of about 1/2 inch per year. If the Eurasian plate is moving south at this rate, how much farther south will London be in 4,000 years?

London will be located 2,000 inches, or about 56 yards,

south of where it is now in 4,000 years.

18. Synthesizing If you had to choose one way for the United States to create energy instead of burning fossil fuels, which would you choose and why? Choose from solar power, nuclear power, hydroelectric power, or wind power.

Answers will vary. Possible answer: solar power. Hydroelectric power

can damage ecosystems; wind turbines are only useful in windy

areas and nuclear power creates nuclear waste that has to be

disposed of. Solar panels are safe and effective and can be attached

to homes and other buildings to heat them and power appliances.

Organizing Concepts

19. Fill in the chart. Tell how each type of rock forms. Give three examples of each type.

Types of Rock

Sedimentary	Metamorphic	Igneous
Formed when fragments or rock or seashells are deposited and buried; also forms from chemical deposits Limestone Shale Sandstone	Formed when high temperature and pressure alter rock Gneiss Hornfels	Formed when molten rock cools Patchwork of crystals Obsidian Pumice Basalt

Unit Test

Reviewing Vocabulary

Complete each sentence with the correct vocabulary word.

1. When warm, moist air rises above cooler air, a severe weather pattern called a(n) _____thunderstorm_____ can form.

2. The counterclockwise rotation of the constellations around the North Star provides evidence of Earth's _____rotation_____.

3. The mixture of gases that surrounds a planet, in which weather takes place, is its _____atmosphere_____.

4. Scientists use the _____astronomical unit_____ to measure distances within the solar system.

5. Daily changes in ocean level at shorelines are _____tides_____.

6. Changes in the appearance of the moon throughout the month are known as _____phases_____.

7. Most _____asteroids_____ lie scattered in orbits between Mars and Jupiter.

8. Two air masses meet along a(n) _____front_____.

9. Belts of high-speed winds found in the upper atmosphere are known as _____jet streams_____.

10. The _____apparent magnitude_____ of a star depends on both the star's distance from Earth and the star's actual brightness.

Checking Main Ideas

For each statement, circle the word *True* or the word *False*.
Rewrite each false statement to make it true.

11. Water cools and heats faster than land.

True   (False)

Land cools and heats faster than water.

12. The Moon's gravitational pull on Earth causes the Coriolis effect.

True   (False)

The Moon's gravitational pull on Earth causes tides.

13. Four of the five outer planets have rings.

(True)   False

_____

14. All of the stars in a galaxy are main-sequence stars.

True   (False)

Most of the stars in a galaxy are main-sequence stars.

15. A solar eclipse can be viewed from all unclouded areas of Earth's sky.

True   (False)

A lunar eclipse can be viewed from all unclouded areas of Earth's sky.

16. Doppler radar can be used to track the movement of storms and weather.

(True)   False

_____

Name _____ Date _____

Using Inquiry Skills

Answer the questions using complete sentences.

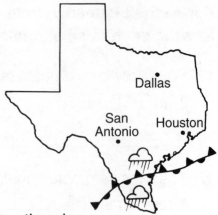

17. **Predict** Write a brief weather forecast for southern Texas based on the weather map.

There is a stationary front in southern

Texas. The weather will remain rainy in

the near future.

18. **Infer** It is easier to correct image distortions in mirrors than in lenses. How do you think this has affected telescopes?

Most large telescopes are reflecting telescopes because it is

easier to modify the shape of a mirror to reduce image distortion.

19. **Hypothesize** In 1982 and 1983, abnormally warm water led to the death or migration of many fish along the Pacific coast of South America. Make a hypothesis about why this happened.

An El Niño event occurred, bringing unusually warm water

to the coast of South America.

20. **Compare** How are solar and lunar eclipses alike? How are they different?

Both occur when Earth and the Moon are aligned with the Sun. A lunar

eclipse occurs when the Moon passes into Earth's shadow. A solar eclipse

occurs when the Moon blocks the Sun's light and casts a shadow on Earth.

Thinking Critically

Answer the questions using complete sentences.

21. **Apply** If humans were to establish a colony on Mars, what challenging conditions would they face? What features might help them survive?

   Mars has no oxygen, its gravity is much less than the gravity on Earth, and it has enormous dust storms. The polar ice caps on Mars might provide fresh water.

22. **Evaluate** You fly a kite during the day near a seashore. In what direction will the kite probably move? Explain your answer.

   The kite will probably move from the direction of the ocean toward land. During the day, a sea breeze blows cooler air from the ocean toward land.

23. **Draw Conclusions** Earth has moderate temperatures in which life can thrive. The Moon, which is about the same distance from the Sun, experiences temperature extremes. Explain why.

   Earth has an atmosphere which allows radiation from the Sun to pass through and warm its surface. Gases such as water vapor and carbon dioxide trap the heat. The Moon has no atmosphere so all the heat escapes into space.

24. **Synthesize** A weather balloon is launched into the atmosphere. Describe the changes in the air pressure that the balloon will detect as it passes up through the atmosphere.

   The weather balloon will record that the air pressure decreases with increasing altitude.

Name _____ Date _____

Organizing Concepts

25. Complete the star life cycles.

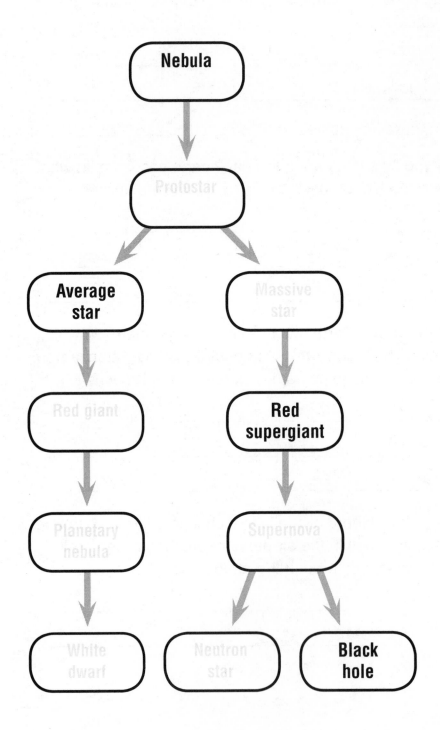

Unit E Test

Reviewing Vocabulary

Write the letter of the correct definition next to each vocabulary word.

___d___ 1. electron

___h___ 2. Periodic Table

___f___ 3. chemical equation

___b___ 4. pH

___c___ 5. condensation

___e___ 6. proton

___a___ 7. solution

___g___ 8. pressure

a. a mixture that is evenly mixed at the molecular level

b. a measure of the strength of an acid or base

c. the process by which a gas changes to liquid

d. a negatively charged particle that surrounds an atom's nucleus

e. a positively charged particle inside an atom's nucleus

f. a way of showing the substances that react and form in a chemical reaction

g. the amount of force applied over a specific area

h. a chart of the elements arranged by atomic number

Circle the letter of the correct answer.

9. A substance that cannot be broken down into other substances is called a(n)

A electron

B element

C compound

D mixture

10. A compound is made up of two or more chemically combined

A molecules

B elements

C protons

D electrons

11. The household products shown in the picture are all classified as

A   mixtures

B   bases

C   alloys

(D) acids

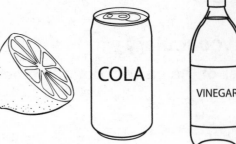

12. During a physical change,

A   energy is absorbed

B   new substances form

(C) matter changes shape, size, or state

D   chemical bonds are broken

Checking Main Ideas

Answer the questions using complete sentences.

13. What is the main difference between a synthesis reaction and a decomposition reaction?

In a synthesis reaction, only one product is formed. In a

decomposition reaction, two or more products are formed.

_____

14. A glass is dropped on the floor and shatters. How do you know that a physical change, and not a chemical change, has taken place?

A physical change is when matter changes size, shape, or

state. No new substances are formed when a glass breaks,

so it is not a chemical change.

15. What is the difference between heat and temperature?

Heat is the transfer of thermal energy from warmer to cooler. Temperature

is the average kinetic energy of the particles in a sample of matter.

16. Chromium has an atomic number of 24 and an atomic mass of 52.00. How many protons are inside the nucleus of a chromium atom?

There are 24 protons, because the atomic number is equal

to the number of protons.

17. Carbon, silicon, and tin are located in the same group in the periodic table. What can you conclude about the properties of these three elements?

The elements must have similar chemical properties.

Using Inquiry Skills

Answer the questions using complete sentences.

18. Use Models Label the parts of the helium atom.

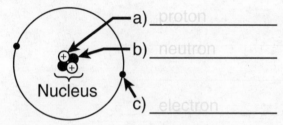

a) proton

b) neutron

Nucleus

c) electron

19. Infer Describe what is happening to the water particles inside the jar.

As the water in the jar cools, the particles

move slower and slower.

20. Use Numbers According to the graph, what is the melting point of water?

Water freezes and melts at 0°C

(32°F).

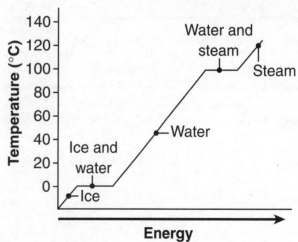

Thinking Critically

Answer the questions using complete sentences.

21. **Evaluate** The diagrams below, labeled A, B, and C, show the movement and arrangement of particles in a solid, a liquid, and a gas. Which diagram represents the gas? How do you know?

A   B   C

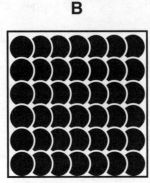 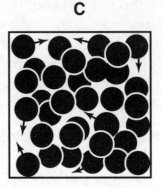

Diagram A represents the gas, because the particles in a

gas move faster and are more spread apart than particles

in solids and liquids.

22. **Apply**   Sam places a tablespoon of baking soda powder into an empty balloon. He then adds a small amount of vinegar to the balloon. In a few seconds, the balloon expands as it fills with gas. Describe how you know that a chemical reaction has taken place inside the balloon.

The gas must be a product of the chemical reaction

between vinegar and baking soda.

_____

_____

Organizing Concepts

23. Complete the organizer.

Acids

- pH range is __0__ to __7__

- have _high_ concentrations of hydrogen atoms

- litmus test _blue_ _litmus turns red_

- have a _sour_ taste

  Examples:
  lemon juice
  battery acid
  stomach acid

Both

- are compounds

- react easily with other substances

- can be dangerous and poisonous

Bases

- pH range is __7__ to __14__

- have _low_ concentrations of hydrogen atoms

- litmus test _red litmus_ _turns blue_

- have a _bitter_ taste

  Examples:
  soap
  bleach
  ammonia

Unit Test

Reviewing Vocabulary

Complete each sentence with the correct vocabulary word.

1. The ___law of conservation of energy___ states that energy can change form, but it cannot be created or destroyed.

2. Stored energy is called ___potential energy___ .

3. ___Lasers___ produce light that is only one color.

4. The range of colors that make up white light is called the ___visible spectrum___ .

5. ___Insulators___ are materials that do not conduct electricity well.

Match each definition to the correct vocabulary word.

6. Device that transforms mechanical energy into electrical energy ⟶ friction

7. Device that transforms electrical energy into mechanical energy ⟶ joule

8. Unit of measurement also called a Newton-meter ⟶ mechanical advantage

9. The force that opposes the motion of one surface against another ⟶ electric motor

10. The amount by which a machine increases applied force ⟶ electric generator

Checking Main Ideas

For each statement, circle the word *True* or the word *False*. Rewrite each false statement to make it true.

11. Rubber, plastic, and glass are examples of good insulators.

(True)   False

_____

12. In this electrical device chemical potential energy is changed directly into mechanical kinetic energy.

True   (False)

The chemical potential energy is changed directly into electrical kinetic energy.

13. Phosphorescent substances, such as ivory and eggshells, produce their own light through a chemical process.

True   (False)

Phosphorescent substances absorb energy from outside light sources and emit some of it as visible light.

14. A convex lens causes light rays to converge at a focal point.

(True)   False

_____

15. Radiation, convection, and conduction are ways that electricity can be transferred.

True   (False)

Radiation, convection, and conduction are ways that thermal energy can be transferred.

Answer the questions using complete sentences.

16. What are the three main properties of a wave?

wavelength, frequency, and amplitude

17. Describe two things that Sir Isaac Newton concluded about color from his prism experiments.

Answers may vary. White light is a mixture of all colors. A prism separates white light into the seven colors that make it up. Individual colors of light cannot be further separated.

18. What class of lever is shown in the picture? How does it work?

It is a first-class lever. A first-class lever is a simple machine that has an arm that moves around a pivot point called a fulcrum. The lever works by changing the direction and/or the amount of force needed.

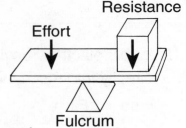

19. Name two examples of waves. Tell how each wave is created.

Answers may vary. seismic waves, created by energy released during an earthquake; electromagnetic waves, such as visible light, and radio waves created by electromagnetic energy; sound waves, created when objects vibrate

Using Inquiry Skills

Answer the questions using complete sentences.

20. **Classify** Complete the chart using items from the box.

wheelbarrow	nutcracker	screwdriver	ramp
fishing rod	axe	see-saw	shovel
bottle opener	bicycle gears	metal screw	wedge
doorknob	crowbar		

Inclined Plane	First-Class Lever	Second-Class Lever	Third-Class Lever	Wheel and Axle
ramp	see-saw	wheelbarrow	fishing rod	bicycle gears
metal screw	crowbar	nutcracker	shovel	screwdriver
wedge		bottle opener		doorknob
axe				

21. **Infer** A funhouse at the school carnival has convex mirrors, concave mirrors, and crinkled aluminum foil mirrors. What effect does each type of mirror have on a person's reflection?

The convex mirrors cause light from an object to spread apart when it leaves the mirror producing an image that is smaller. The concave mirrors cause light from an object to converge producing an image that is magnified. The crinkled aluminum foil causes light rays to reflect at different angles producing a diffuse reflection with no clear image.

22. **Compare** What is the difference between a longitudinal wave and a transverse wave?

In a longitudinal wave, the motion of the particles in the medium is back and forth, parallel to the direction of motion of the wave. In a transverse wave, the motion of the particles is up and down, perpendicular to the direction of motion of the wave.

Thinking Critically
Answer the questions using complete sentences.

23. **Synthesize** Is it possible for an electric motor to run on both AC and DC? Explain why or why not.

Answers may vary. No; In an AC motor, the poles of the armature are always reversing. In a DC motor, a commutator is needed to allow the poles to be reversed.

24. **Hypothesize** At a parade a trombone player marches past you playing one long note. The pitch of the note does not change as the trombone player passes. Was there a Doppler effect? Why?

Yes; There was a Doppler effect, but the trombone player was not moving fast enough for me to detect it.

Organizing Concepts

25. Complete the flowchart using words and phrases from the box.

conduction	thermal energy	as heat by	radiation
from warmer to cooler		convection	is transferred

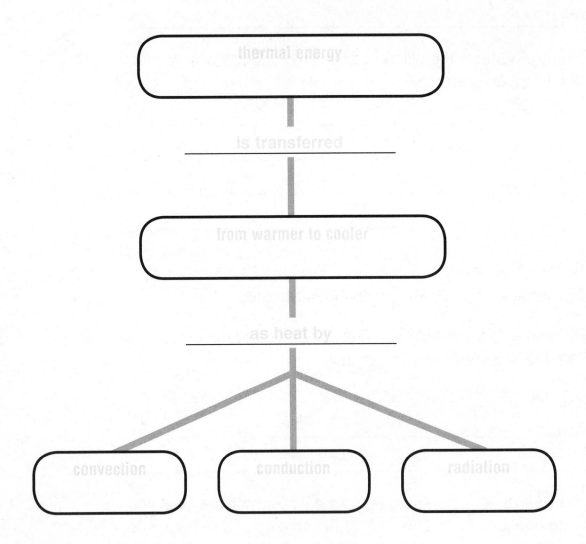

thermal energy

is transferred

from warmer to cooler

as heat by

convection · conduction · radiation

Classifying Organisms

Materials

- pen or pencil

Class Time

10–20 minutes

Grouping

Independent

Skills Focus

Classifying, Analyzing Data, Inferring

Procedure

Tell students they will complete a table and analyze information to demonstrate what they have learned about classifying organisms. Pass out the test sheets. Read the instructions together as a class. Encourage students to be as specific as possible when completing the chart about the characteristics of different organisms. Observe students as they work. For step two, encourage students to include explanations for their answers.

Assess Performance

Check that students accurately and completely filled out the table of organism characteristics. Check that students have correctly analyzed the data presented in step 2 and made the correct inference. Check that students have provided an explanation for their inference. Oral descriptions should include explanations of why the student classified the organisms as he or she did.

Classifying Organisms

Concept: Organisms can be classified into broad groups based on certain characteristics.

Assessed Items	Points	What to Look For
Classification Chart	3	All cells of the table are complete and correct.
	2	Some cells of the table are incomplete or inaccurate.
	1	Most cells of the table are incomplete or inaccurate.
Analyzing Data	3	All inferences are correct and completely explained.
	2	Two of the inferences are incorrect or not explained.
	1	Three or more of the inferences are incorrect or not explained.
Oral Presentation	3	Student's responses show good preparedness for oral follow-up.
	2	Student's responses are adequate for oral follow-up.
	1	Student's responses show that he or she is unprepared for oral follow-up.

Name _____ Date _____

Classifying Organisms

Organisms can be classified into broad groups based on certain characteristics. Do you know the characteristics of different groups of organisms?

Procedure

1. Complete the classification chart. Fill in as many details as possible. For example: within a group, if different organisms have different ways of obtaining food, include all of the different ways organisms in that group can obtain food.

	Single cell or many cells?	Nucleus present or absent?	How does it obtain food?	Movement?	Examples
Bacteria	single cell	absent	some make their own food; some consume food	no	E. coli, Archaebacteria, Eubacteria, spirochetes, bacilli, cocci
Protist	single cell and many cells	present	some make their own food; some consume food	yes	Paramecium, Amoeba, algae, slime mold
Fungi	single cell and many cells	present	absorb food from environment	no	mushrooms
Plant	many cells	present	most make their own food	no	any plant
Animal	many cells	present	consumes food	yes	any animal

2. The characteristics of two different mystery organisms are shown below. Determine the group to which each organism belongs. Explain how you made each classification.

	Single cell or many cells?	Nucleus present or absent?	How does it obtain food?	Movement?
Mystery Organism A	single cell	present	consumes food	yes
Mystery Organism B	many cells	present	makes its own food	no

To which kingdom does Organism A belong? Why?

It belongs to the protist kingdom, because it has all of the

characteristics of that group.

To which kingdom does Organism B belong? Why?

It belongs to the plant kingdom, because it has all of the

characteristics of that group.

Food Energy

Materials

- pen or pencil

Class Time

20–30 minutes

Grouping

Independent

Skills Focus

Comparing, Inferring, Analyzing

Procedure

Tell students that they will do an activity to demonstrate what they have learned about the cycling of energy in ecosystems. Pass out the test sheets. Read the introductory paragraph together as a group. For step 2, students do not have to draw pictures of the organisms in the food chain, although they are encouraged to do so. They can use words instead.

Assess Performance

Circulate around the room as students work. Check that their food chains have exactly four links, but do not help them construct the food chains. Also, check to see that the arrows of the food chain are pointing in the direction from which energy is passed. A common mistake is to show the arrows pointing in the opposite direction. When students get to step 3, remind them that they should complete the energy pyramid using the plants and animals from their food chain. For step 4, students should write the percentage of energy that is available at each trophic level.

Food Energy

Concept: In an ecosystem, energy moves in one direction through different trophic levels. An energy pyramid is a model that shows how energy moves from one level to another. More energy is available at lower trophic levels than at higher trophic levels.

Assessed Items	Points	What to Look For
Food Chain	3	Food chain is complete and accurate. Food chain includes a producer, primary consumer, secondary consumer, and tertiary consumer.
	2	Food chain is mostly accurate. Food chain includes a producer, primary consumer, secondary consumer, and tertiary consumer, but may not be in correct order.
	1	Food chain is incomplete and/or inaccurate. Food chain does not include four trophic levels and is not drawn correctly.
Energy Pyramid	3	Energy pyramid is complete and accurate. Student correctly used organisms from food chain to complete energy pyramid. Trophic levels and percentages of energy available labeled correctly.
	2	Energy pyramid is mostly complete and accurate. Student correctly used organisms from food chain to complete energy pyramid. Most trophic levels and percentages of energy available labeled correctly, but there are some mistakes.
	1	Energy pyramid is incomplete and inaccurate. Student may have used organisms from food chain, but they are incorrectly placed in energy pyramid. Most trophic levels and percentages of energy available labeled incorrectly.

Name _____ Date _____

Food Energy

In an ecosystem, energy moves in one direction, from producers to consumers. Each step in the movement of energy is known as a trophic level. In this activity, you will make an energy pyramid to show how energy might move from one level to another in a desert ecosystem.

Procedure

1. Read the chart below, which lists the names of common desert plants and animals.

Animals and Plants in a Desert Ecosystem

Organism	Description
sagebrush	woody shrub with silvery leaves that stay green all year
prickly pear cactus	low succulent plant with flat, fleshy pads that store water
squirrel	diet includes seeds and leaves
bat	diet includes insects
badger	diet includes chipmunks, insects, birds, grass, and nuts
mountain lion	diet includes pronghorn antelopes and other grazers
coyote	diet includes lizards and pronghorn antelopes
raptor	diet includes snakes, lizards, and squirrels
insect	desert insects feed on a variety of plants

2. Using plants and animals from the chart, draw a desert food chain with four links on the back of this page. Your food chain must contain a producer, a primary consumer, a secondary consumer, and a tertiary consumer.
Check students' food chains.

3. Use your food chain from step 2 to complete the energy pyramid. Label the levels of the energy pyramid with the names of the trophic levels. Write the names of the animals and plants from your food chain in the correct trophic level.

4. On the energy pyramid, show what happens to energy as it moves from lower to higher trophic levels. Mark the percentage of energy available at each trophic level. The first one has been done for you.

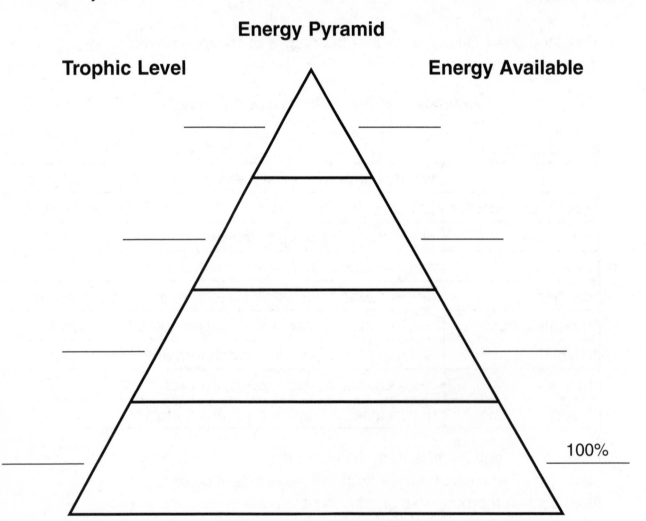

Energy Pyramid

Trophic Level   **Energy Available**

100%

Where Are the Tectonic Plate Boundaries of the World?

Materials

- colored pencils
- paper

Class Time

20–30 minutes

Grouping

Pairs

Skills Focus

Comparing, Interpreting Data, Analyzing

Procedure

Tell students that they will do an activity to demonstrate what they have learned about earthquakes, volcanoes, and tectonic plates. Pass out the test sheets and read the instructions together. Have your class split up into pairs, or assign pairs if necessary. Observe students as they work. Remind students of the definitions of convergent boundaries, divergent boundaries, and transform fault boundaries. Ask them to think about if and how this pattern of earthquakes has affected where people have built cities, and population density in general. When all of your students are finished filling out the activity sheet, engage the classroom in an oral discussion about how they filled out their sheets. Also ask them to guess the names of the plates, based on the continents that are situated on them. Call on as many students as possible and engage them in a discussion of the different types of plate boundaries, volcanoes and earthquakes, and how humans are affected by these natural disasters.

Assess Performance

Check that students have accurately and completely traced the tectonic plates. Make sure that they have correctly named the types of plate boundaries; mountain ranges are often convergent boundaries, the sites of earthquakes are often transform fault boundaries, and many mid-ocean ridges are divergent boundaries. Make sure that the landforms are correctly tied to their corresponding plate boundaries.

Assessment Resources

115

Where Are the Tectonic Plate Boundaries of the World?

Concept: The lithosphere of the earth is broken up into sections called tectonic plates. The part of the mantle beneath the lithosphere is molten. The tectonic plates (upon which continents sit) float on this molten layer.

Assessed Items	Points	What to Look For
Worksheet	3	All of the tectonic plates have been correctly drawn onto the worksheet.
	2	Some of the tectonic plates have been correctly drawn onto the worksheet.
	1	Most of the tectonic plates have not been drawn correctly on the worksheet.
Map	3	The student has correctly indicated all of the types of plate boundaries.
	2	The student has correctly indicated some of the types of plate boundaries.
	1	The student has correctly indicated few or none of the types of plate boundaries.
Oral Presentation	3	Student's responses during class discussion of the activity show good preparedness and understanding.
	2	Student's responses are adequate for oral discussion.
	1	Student's responses show that he or she is unprepared for oral follow-up.

Where Are the Tectonic Plate Boundaries of the World?

Slowly but surely, the continents drift toward each other or spread farther apart, on their tectonic plates. Earthquakes and volcanoes are common along plate boundaries. Can you use the locations of earthquakes and volcanoes to determine the shapes and sizes of the plates?

Procedure

1. Look at the map below, which shows the locations of earthquakes and volcanoes around the world. Volcanoes are shown by triangles. Earthquakes are shown by dots. With your partner, decide where you think the plate boundaries are located. Draw them on the map, with a colored pencil.

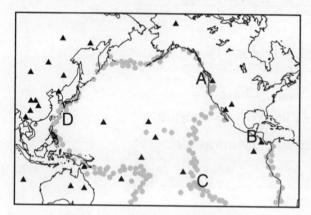

2. Discuss what types of boundaries you think are located at each of the four locations on the map, labeled A, B, C, and D. Describe the landforms and other information that led you and your partner to determine the types of boundaries.

Location A

What type of plate boundary do you think this is?

transform fault boundary

_____

_____

What landforms made you think it was this type of boundary?

What else made you think it was this type of boundary?

There is a fault; earthquakes
_____

_____

Location B

What type of plate boundary do you think this is?

divergent boundary
_____

What landforms made you think it was this type of boundary?

What else made you think it was this type of boundary?

It is a mid-ocean ridge.
_____

_____

Location C

What type of plate boundary do you think this is?

divergent boundary
_____

What landforms made you think it was this type of boundary?

What else made you think it was this type of boundary?

There is a rift valley.
_____

_____

Location D

What type of plate boundary do you think this is?

convergent boundary
_____

What landforms made you think it was this type of boundary?

What else made you think it was this type of boundary?

There is an ocean trench where on plate dives beneath

another.
_____

Galaxy Journal

Materials

- pen or pencil

Class Time

20–30 minutes

Grouping

Independent

Skills Focus

Classifying, Communicating, Recording Data

Procedure

Tell students that they will do an activity to demonstrate what they have learned about the solar system and the Milky Way. Pass out the test sheets. Read the instructions together as a class. Observe students as they work. For step 1, encourage students to remember what they learned about the planets and other objects in the solar system. For step 2, encourage students to think about the three main parts of the Milky Way and the objects that make up the Milky Way.

Assess Performance

Check that students listed in their charts each of the nine planets in addition to asteroids, comets, and meteoroids. They should list two characteristics of each object. Charts of Milky Way features should list its three parts—the bulge, the halo, and the disk. The charts also should include stars at various stages in their life cycles. Older stars are located in the bulge, and younger stars in the disk.

Galaxy Journal

Concept: The solar system and Milky Way are made up of many parts.

Assessed Items	Points	What to Look For
Solar System Objects	3	Student listed all nine planets, comets, asteroids, and meteoroids.
	2	Student listed most of the nine planets as well as other bodies. Some objects left off list.
	1	Student's list is incomplete or inaccurate. Many objects left off list.
Describe objects in the solar system	3	Student recorded two characteristics of each object in the solar system. The characteristics listed are accurate.
	2	Student recorded an average of one characteristic per object in the solar system. Most characteristics listed are accurate.
	1	Student recorded few characteristics of the objects in the solar system. Most characteristics listed are inaccurate.
List features of the Milky Way	3	Student listed the three parts of the Milky Way, and mentioned older stars in the bulge and young stars in the disk.
	2	Student listed one or two parts of the Milky Way. He or she also listed other stars, but did not mention the various stages in their life cycles.
	1	Student's list of the parts of the Milky Way is inaccurate and failed to mention other stars.

Galaxy Journal

Our solar system is made up of many parts. It is part of the Milky Way galaxy. Do you know the objects in the solar system and the parts of the Milky Way galaxy?

Procedure

1. Complete the chart with the names of the objects in the solar system. Name at least two characteristics of each object.

Objects in the Solar System	
Planets	**Characteristics**
Mercury	closest planet to the Sun; very hot during the day and very cold at night
Venus	thick atmosphere; very hot day and night
Earth	only planet known to support life; liquid water on surface
Mars	has polar ice caps; has canyons, mountains, and volcanoes
Jupiter	largest planet; has many moons
Saturn	has complex ring system; active atmosphere
Uranus	has a blue-green color; gravity similar to Earth
Neptune	has blue color; very cold all year long
Pluto	most distant planet; smallest planet

Minor Objects	
asteroids	irregularly shaped rocks; most lie between Mars and Jupiter
meteoroids	small rocky objects; can enter Earth's atmosphere and burn up, forming "shooting stars"
comets	frozen balls of ice and rock that orbit the Sun

2. What are the parts of the Milky Way? Complete the chart. What objects do you find in the various parts?

The Milky Way	
Parts of the Milky Way	**Objects Found**
bulge	center of the galaxy; region of gases, dust, and stars that have nearly completed their life cycles
halo	encircles the bulge; made of old stars and dark matter
disk	made up of the spiral arms that spread outward from the bulge; contains young stars

Chemical and Physical Changes

Materials

- pen or pencil

Class Time

30 minutes

Grouping

Independent

Preparation

Procedure

Distribute the test sheets to students. Read the activity title and the opening paragraph together as a class. Review the directions and the list of matter changes. You may wish to provide students with more detail about each matter change, or talk about other common matter changes that are not listed. If students are not familiar with some of the matter changes on the list, tell them that they may add any additional matter changes that they know about.

Assess Performance

As students work, circulate around the room and question them about the matter changes they are placing in their charts. Have students provide brief oral explanations for why they classified the matter changes as they did. Make sure that students' charts list five chemical changes and five physical changes.

Chemical and Physical Changes

Concepts: In a physical change, matter changes shape, size, or state, but no new substances form. During a chemical change, one set of substances change to form new substances.

Assessed Items	Points	What to Look For
Chart	3	Chart is complete; ten changes listed; five physical changes and five chemical changes.
	2	Chart is mostly complete; some boxes unfilled.
	1	Chart is mostly incomplete; many boxes unfilled.
Classification	3	All ten matter changes are classified correctly as chemical or physical.
	2	Most of the matter changes are classified correctly; some mistakes.
	1	Most of the matter changes are classified incorrectly.
Reasoning	3	Student provided solid, logical reasoning for all ten classifications.
	2	Student provided solid, logical reasoning for some of the classifications.
	1	Reasons for classifications mostly incorrect.
Oral Answers	3	Student expresses specific, accurate information and demonstrates a clear understanding of physical and chemical changes.
	2	Student is able to provide accurate explanations for some, but not all, classifications.
	1	Student reasoning is mostly inaccurate and does not demonstrate an understanding of physical and chemical changes.

Name _____ Date _____

Chemical and Physical Changes

You will be given a list of common matter changes that happen around you every day. Can you tell which ones are chemical changes and which ones are physical changes?

Procedure

1. Study the list of matter changes. Think about each change. Have you ever seen or experienced this change in matter? What did you observe as the change was taking place?

Common Matter Changes

- baking rolls
- ripening of tomatoes
- ice cube breaking into pieces
- rusting of iron
- egg whites turning from clear to white when cooked
- leaves changing color
- milk turning sour
- yellowing of old newspaper
- popcorn popping
- logs burning in fireplace
- dissolving sugar in lemonade
- water changing to steam
- plant making food
- freezing water
- tearing of notebook paper

2. Choose 10 changes from the list. In the chart below, classify each change as either a chemical change or a physical change. Your chart must have five chemical changes and five physical changes.

3. For each matter change you list, give a reason for why you classified it as physical or chemical.

Matter Change	Physical or Chemical?	Reason
1.		
2.		
3.		
4.		
5.		
6.		
7.		
8.		
9.		
10.		

Matter changes chosen may vary.
Chemical changes: baking rolls, ripening of tomatoes, rusting of iron, leaves changing color, milk turning sour, yellowing of old newspaper, logs burning in fireplace, plant making food
Physical changes: ice cube breaking into pieces, egg whites turning white, popcorn popping, dissolving sugar in lemonade, water changing to steam, freezing water, tearing of notebook paper

May the Force Be with You

Materials

- string
- spring scales
- books of equal size

Class Time

30–45 minutes

Grouping

Independent

Skills Focus

Predicting, Hypothesizing, Analyzing Data

Procedure

Tell students that they will be doing an activity to demonstrate what they learned about Newton's second law of motion. Pass out the test sheets and the materials. Read the instructions together as a class. Observe students as they work. Suggest that students think about all the factors that influence force, such as mass.

Assess Performance

Check that students accurately predicted that the greater the mass, the greater the force needed to move the books. Observe students as they conduct their experiments. Remind them to measure the force needed to keep the books moving, not the starting force used to overcome friction. Circulate around the room as students summarize their findings. Students' responses should demonstrate a good understanding of the concepts emphasized in the chapter.

May the Force Be with You

Concept: Newton's second law of motion describes the relationships among force (*F*), mass (*m*), and acceleration (*a*). This relationship can be written as $F = m \times a$. In this activity, students will demonstrate that this law shows that the greater the mass of an object, the greater is the force needed to move it.

Assessed Items	Points	What to Look For
Predictions	3	Predictions are clearly based on the mass of the books. Student shows a good understanding of unit concepts.
	2	Predictions based on the mass of the books. Student shows some understanding of unit concepts.
	1	Predictions are not based on the mass of each object(s). Shows little or no understanding of unit concepts.
Experiment	3	Student followed directions and recorded data accurately.
	2	Student did not follow all the directions or did not record data accurately.
	1	Student did not follow directions and did not record data accurately.
Essay Question	3	Student's response is comprehensive and shows a complete understanding of Newton's second law of motion.
	2	Parts of student's response are unclear or unorganized and/or show a partial understanding of Newton's second law of motion.
	1	Most of response is unclear and/or unorganized and shows little understanding of Newton's second law of motion.

Name _____ Date _____

May the Force Be with You

Newton's second law of motion describes the relationships among force, mass, and acceleration. In this activity, you will explore these relationships.

Procedure

1. Predict how much force you think will be needed to move each group of books. Rate the amount of force needed on a scale of 1–10, with 1 being very little force and 10 being a lot of force.

Force (1 to 10)	
	1 book
	2 books
	4 books

2. Tie a string around a single book. Attach a spring scale to the string. Now pull the book slowly along a smooth table surface. How much force was needed to keep the book moving? Record the data in the chart below.

	Newtons of Force
1 book	
2 books	
4 books	

3. Repeat step 2 for the two other groups of books.

Results

3. Did the outcomes of your experiment match your predictions? Write a short paragraph about what you learned. How does this experiment relate to Newton's second law of motion?

_____

_____

_____

_____

_____

_____